SWORDS CEREBUS

Volume Four

Aardvark Vanaheim Inc.

First Printing: Fall, 1982
Second Printing: Summer, 1985
Third Printing: Spring, 1986

also available:
Swords of Cerebus Vol. 1
Swords of Cerebus Vol. 2
Swords of Cerebus Vol. 3
Swords of Cerebus Vol. 5
Swords of Cerebus Vol. 6

Printed in Canada

ISBN 0-919359-03-5

INTRODUCTIONS

"Magiking" (previously unpublished)

"Black Magiking" (Cerebus No. 13, Dec. 1979 - Jan. 1980)

I was contacted by a Hamilton cartoonist (Ian Carr) to do a ten to twelve page Cerebus story for The 1981 Comics Annual (a project which was aborted, hence the first appearance of the story here.) At the time I was still doing Cerebus on a bi-monthly schedule, drawing the book one month and filling the rest of my time with mondo bizarro commercial shit ("shit" is a technical word used in the commercial art field to cover those "fun" art jobs like, say, a tire ad or a flyer advertising a disco opening). Any chance to fill my time with more comic book (and especially Cerebus-related) jobs was welcome indeed. It also rather neatly solved a problem I had been having with a major point I was trying to develop in the book - the stasis created in Estarcion by most of it's major forces existing in opposition to one another. Be it politics, magic, wealth, religion, each force tends to have a major opposing force. I had planned "Black Magiking" to show that the Lower Feldan countryside had its fair share of magical forces and beings and situations, almost completely unheard of in the major metropolitan capitals. I was torn on the question of alluding to the good magician. Should I drag him in for a couple of panels, or split the story in two? Or just make a few pertinent footnotes?

Now I had ten to twelve pages to develop a completely different story. The fact that I was asked to gear the story to the "eleven to thirteen year olds" even allowed for a more vivid contrast in the two magician characters. The lightweight "Magiking" reads like a child's fable with a kind of cotton candy look. "Black Magiking" is far grimmer as Cerebus stories go, opening in a typical Lower Feldan riverside village where the resident priest is a kind of combination mayor/judge/counsellor/ chieftain/dictator. The inhabitants are basically those same lovable villagers who were never too busy to wander up the hill in the dead of night to visit Dr. Frankenstein. Self-centered, xeno-phobic, paranoid, quarrelsome, and myopic. If you tell them to, they'll be happy to throw some tea into the harbour just to break up the monotony of their day to day lives. ("Crop's in. Expect winter'll be along in a few weeks.")

As for Necross the (ha ha ha) Mad. He was cut from whole cloth; Exidor from *Mork and Mindy* (did anybody at *all* watch the second and third seasons?) He was a very bouncy character, which I hadn't realized until I had a few pages done. Much like the Moon Roach would later, he led me to develop almost a completely different style in order to capture the kind of broad gestures and body movements of a real nutbar.

The ending on this thirty-one page story is pretty flat. I was not yet really capable of really pacing out twenty pages. As I drew the confrontation with the priest and villagers of Theyr facing Necross and then Thrunk, I kept coming up with lines I desperately wanted in the book. I identified so much with the villagers, engaged with this great struggle with the forces of evil, but still quibbling over who gets the crops when they get back to the village. The

ending finally got squeezed into two panels.

By the way – the castle that looks like a huge Black Tower? Remember the Black Tower Empire that I kept mentioning? Well, it has nothing to do with that.

THE SQUARE BENEATH HIM SEEMED TO SWELL AND TWIST AND BECOME SOLID AS STARS SWIRLED AROUND HIM...

IN THE NEXT FEW MOMENTS, HE BEGAN TO *ACCELERATE*, END-OVER-END UNTIL...

CEREBUS AWOKE TO A SENSATION OF *FALLING*...

WAM

"MAGIKING"

WHEN HIS VISION *CLEARED*, HE WAS ON, RATHER THAN *IN*, A ROOM, FOR THERE WERE NO WALLS... ONLY A ROUGH STONE FLOOR THAT AT LEAST *SEEMED* FIRM...

... AND A FEW NARROW STEPS VANISHING INTO THE STARRY BLACKNESS THAT SURROUNDED HIM

ABRUPTLY, A *DISEMBODIED* LEG APPEARED FROM NOWHERE...

RAXUS SAXUS ROMANO DAY IPSO-TIPSO TEMPUS AWAY...

FOUR LONG TINS THAT ROLL HOMELY HEAVEN'S KNEES NOW COME NISH

BY THE BEARD OF Z'HIN Z'HOMLIE I'LL GIVE IT A TRY!

UH-HUH!

MMMM... ...YES...

AHA!

EITHER YOU'RE TEN PERCENT FUR AND NINETY PERCENT SILLY PUTTY

...OR I'VE BEEN LOOKING IN THE WRONG BOOK.

AHA!

AARDVARKS!

"AARDVARKS ...SNOUT, TAIL, THREE CLAWS ...THREE FINGERS OPPOSABLE THUMB"

MM-HM MM-HM

"MONOLITH PEOPLES, AARDVARK FABLES OF ... CONTRIBUTION TO FROZEN FOOD"

"AARDVARKS AND AELNAP, SILVER DYNASTY AND LATER..."

"CAUSES OF AARDVARK FAMINE"

DIAMONDBACK, APRICOT BRANDY...,"

AH! MAGICAL PROPERTIES.

"THE AARDVARK IS THE MOST POWERFUL OF THE..."

*!

DO--DO YOU KNOW WHAT YOU ARE?

YOU MEAN BESIDES BEING AWFULLY ANGRY?

OH.

THE SPELL ... DREADFULLY SORRY

NOT AT ALL...

CEREBUS JUST WASN'T USED TO FEELING THAT WAY WITHOUT THE AID OF SEVERAL TANKARDS OF ALE...

PERHAPS I SHOULD **EXPLAIN**...

"A FEW CENTURIES AGO, MAGIC FLOURISHED IN THE WORLD... DEVELOPMENTS CAME QUICKLY FOR SOME REASON... ANSWERS TO RIDDLES UNGUESSED FOR MILLENIA BECAME READILY APPARENT! ABILITIES THAT HAD BEEN THE PROVINCE OF THE MOST PROFICIENT BECAME CHILD'S PLAY FOR THE **HUMBLEST** CONJUROR! FOR A TIME, MAGIC ENJOYED A **RENAISSANCE**..."

"COMPETITION WAS FIERCE AS EACH MAGICIAN STROVE TO OUTDO THE OTHER IN HIS MAGIC..."

"BUT, EVIL MAGICIANS, TOO, ENJOYED A GOLDEN AGE... AND, IN TIME, ONE OF THESE FOUND THE KEY TO UNLIMITED POWER! A WISER MAGICIAN WOULD HAVE EXERCISED CAUTION, BUT, DRUNK WITH POWER, HE UNLEASHED THE FULL FORCE OF HIS **CREATION**"

THE RESULTING INFERNO ERASED HIS POWERS! SO FAR-FLUNG WAS THE EFFECT THAT ONLY A HANDFUL OF MAGICIANS ESCAPED... OTHERS WERE REDUCED TO ABILITIES OF **MASS HYPNOTISM** AND **CONJURE**...

BY UNSPOKEN AGREEMENT, GOOD MAGICIANS WHO WERE UNAFFECTED LOCATED NEAR THEIR EVIL COUNTERPARTS TO PREVENT WIDE-SCALE ABUSE OF THE POWER THAT REMAINED...

HMM!

THINK! THINK!

AHA! I'M *GOOD*, BECAUSE THE MAGICIAN I'M GUARDING AGAINST IS *EVIL*!

BUT THAT'S *ANOTHER* QUESTION YOU CAN'T ANSWER...

...WHAT MAKES *HIM* EVIL?

WHAT MAKES HIM *EVIL*?!

HE WEARS BLACK ALL THE TIME

HE TALKS WITH HIS MOUTH FULL

HE NEVER BRUSHES HIS TEETH

HE STAYS OUT ALL NIGHT... HE NEVER FINISHES HIS *VEGETABLES*

YOU DON'T NEED A *MAGICAL WEAPON*...

WHAT YOU NEED IS A *BABY-SITTER*!

A MAGICIAN'S LIFE-SPAN IS FIVE OR SIX THOUSAND *YEARS*...

EITHER YOU HELP ME...

...OR I'LL KEEP YOU HERE DEBATING GOOD AND EVIL UNTIL YOUR FUR TURNS WHITE

THE PULSATING LIGHT SUBSIDES! THE MAGICIAN IS DRAINED BY THE ORDEAL...

BUT AT LEAST NOW HE HAD HIS...

...WEAPON?

MAGICIAN?

FULLY AWAKE NOW, CEREBUS REALIZED HE WAS BACK AGAIN WHERE HE HAD *BEGUN*...

...PENNILESS AND ADRIFT ON THE FELD RIVER!

A DREAM? OR DID THE MAGICIAN NOW HAVE HIS ULTIMATE WEAPON OF *"UNMATCHED MIGHT"*?

THE FIRST BREATH OF SUMMER IN LOWER FELDA...

A SOLITARY BIRD, WINGS OVER THE LUSH FARMING LAND FOLLOWING THE COURSE OF THE CLEAR BLUE FELD RIVER...

AND WHETHER IT IS **COGNIZANT** OF THE FACT OR NOT...

IT BECOMES YET ANOTHER LINK IN THE CHAIN OF MISFORTUNE WHICH HAS RECENTLY HOUNDED A CERTAIN EARTH-PIG BORN!

UNHH?

CLOVIS' BLADDER AND BOWELS

AS IF LOWER FELDA HADN'T DONE ENOUGH TO CEREBUS ALREADY!

CEREBUS RECALLS SNATCHES OF A BIZARRE DREAM...A WEAPON OR SOMETHING

HE TRIES NOT TO THINK ABOUT THE BOATLOAD OF GOLD SO RECENTLY LOST IN...

HOLD, CREATURE! AND GIVE AN ACCOUNTING OF YOURSELF

BLACK MAGIKING

AYE, PIEUREU! AS YOU SAID -- A CREATURE OF SORCERY!

CEREBUS IS NO CREATURE OF *SORCERY!*

CEREBUS CONTEMPLATES RUSHING THE LEADER RESTRAINED ONLY BY HIS KNOWLEDGE OF FELD FARMERS...

...AS THE RAW MATERIAL FOR FELDWAR ARMIES THEY ARE RUGGED AND VICIOUS COMBATANTS!

THEN YOUR EXPLAIN YOUR PRESENCE HERE...

...NOW!

CEREBUS HAS JUST BEEN...

LYING DEVIL SPAWN!

CEREBUS BRACES AS THE BULKY FORM HURTLES TOWARD HIM, STAFF RAISED...

THE EARTH-PIG IS NOT ALTOGETHER UNPREPARED FOR THE ATTACK

DISCUSSIONS IN LOWER FELDA HAVE, IN HIS EXPERIENCE, A DISTURBING TENDENCY TO TURN PHYSICAL IN THE BLINKING OF AN EYE...

THE PRISONER IS ACCUSED OF CONSORTING WITH DARK DEMONS, HIGH CRIMES AGAINST NATURAL LAW, MAKING THE CROPS MOULDY, NOT LOOKING LIKE THE REST OF US...

...AND ANYTHING ELSE THE CHURCH OF TARIM CAN THINK OF IN THE COURSE OF THIS TRIAL...

HOW DOES THE PRISONER PLEAD?

CEREBUS DEMANDS THAT YOU RELEASE HIM OR HE'LL CALL UPON HIS DARK MASTERS TO TURN YOU INTO A FLOCK OF PIOUS PINK TOADS...

THAT'S NOT A HALF-BAD DEFENCE.

HE'S BLUFFING.

TRUST ME.

HMPH!

I SAY WE SHOULD EXECUTE HIM NOW AND HAVE THE TRIAL AFTER THE FESTIVAL OF VIRGINS!

I DON'T KNOW ABOUT YOU BUT I DON'T INTEND TO SPEND THE FESTIVAL OF VIRGINS PICKING PINK WARTS OFF MY BACKSIDE

WAIT A MOMENT-- I THINK I HAVE A WAY TO KILL TWO BIRDS WITH ONE STONE...

TARIM HAS LISTENED TO THE CHARGES AND DECLARES NOW THAT *JUSTICE* MUST BE SERVED...

AS PRIEST OF *THEYR* I SHALL SEE TARIM'S WILL IS DONE

EH?

SOME SORT OF...

PRAISE TARIM AND HIS *INFINITE* MERCY!

...*SIGNAL*...

SOME TIME LATER, THE PRIEST APPEARS MOVING AWAY FROM THE VILLAGE AND IT'S FIELDS -- HIS EXPRESSION GRIM AND DETERMINED...

...HE IS FOLLOWED BY ONE OF THE FARMERS WHO CARRIES AN INERT GREY BUNDLE ON ONE SHOULDER...

ABRUPTLY THE GRASSES END. ABRUPTLY THE WINDS DIE AND THERE IS NOTHING SAVE THE COLD GREY ROCK AND THE UNNATURALLY LOUD RUSTLING OF PRIESTLY ROBES...

IT IS CALLED BY MANY NAMES, THIS PLACE OF DARK SILENCE "HELL'S GATE" "HOB'S HOLLOW"-- BUT THE VILLAGERS OF THEYR KNOW IT AS...

...THE CASTLE.

LODGED IN THE VALLEY OF MISTS
IT IS DARK AND UNHOLY HOME TO
NECROSS THE MAD REPUTED TO
BE THE MOST EVIL AND CUNNING
OF THE BLACK SORCERERS...

HIS EVIL IS LEGENDARY IN
LOWER FELDA, CAUSING
CATASTROPHE AFTER CATASTROPHE
--THE BLACK DEATH, THE
AVALANCHE AT SAN TREMAIN,
THE GREAT FIRE OF BEDUIN

NOT TO MENTION THE
PREGNANCY OF ALANNE
THE MILK-MAID...

WHO DIDN'T RELISH THE
IDEA OF BEING FORCED
TO MARRY GUMS, THE
VILLAGE IDIOT...

ARE YOU READY, DESPUESS ... FAVOURED SON OF THE *LIVING TARIM?*

DESPUESS?

SO, MAD NECROSS! YOU SEEK TO ABDUCT A FOLLOWER OF THE LIVING TARIM!

PREPARE YOURSELF NECROSS! VENGEANCE -WILL-BE- **MINE!!**

AS SOON AS I CAN FIND SOMEONE TO GO IN AFTER DESPUESS...

GAZE, THEN, BARBARIAN ON THE FACE OF KAFF ON--
KAFF KAFF THE FACE O--KAFF
WA KAF KAF WATER!!
OUT OF MY WAY, IDIOT! I'M CHOKING
I'VE SIMPLY GOT TO SWITCH TO MIRRORS!
THOSE SMOKEY ENTRANCES ARE MURDER ON THE BRONCHIAL PASSAGES...

SO-- YOU'RE NECROSS THE MAD?

NECROSS THE MAD, EH? HAHAHAAH HAHAAHAA HAHAHAAH HAHAHAHA

AND WHAT MAKES YOU THINK I'M NECROSS HA HAHA THE MAD?

JUST A WILD GUESS.

MAD, IS IT? MAD? I ASK YOU-- IS...

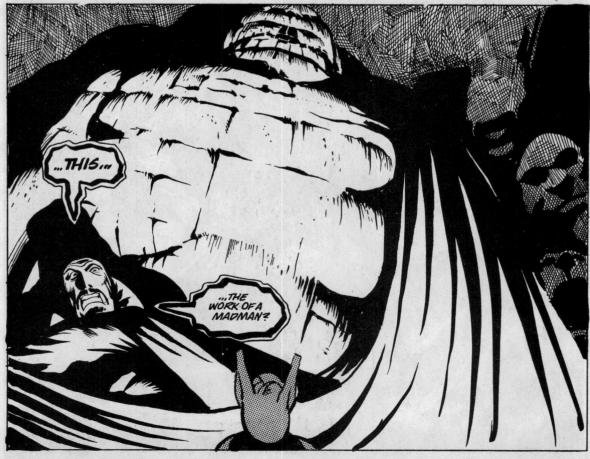

...THIS...

...THE WORK OF A MADMAN?

CEREBUS COULDN'T SAY -- SIXTEEN-FOOT PAPERWEIGHTS AREN'T ORDINARILY REGARDED AS PROOF OF SANITY!

PAPERWEIGHT? *PAPERWEIGHT?* EVEN FOR A SHORT, GREY FURRY PERSON YOU'RE UNUSUALLY *NAIVE!*

THIS IS *THRUNK!* MY GREATEST CREATION

SOMEDAY, I'LL BREATHE LIFE INTO MY STONE *THRUNK*

...AND THEN

AND THEN!

AND THEN *WHAT?*

I HAVEN'T THE *FOGGIEST*

THAT'S WHY I'M A LITTLE RELUCTANT TO BREATHE LIFE INTO HIM...

CEREBUS ALWAYS FEELS OUT-OF-PLACE ASKING INTELLIGENT QUESTIONS IN *LOWER FELDA*...

THE PRIEST WHO BROUGHT YOU HERE WILL BE BACK-- YOU CAN COUNT ON IT!

SEEKING TO DESTROY ME WITH HIS CHANTS AND INVOCATIONS...

THE FOOLS! ALWAYS BLAMING ME FOR THEIR EARTHQUAKES, THEIR FIRES -- *ALWAYS* BLAMING ME FOR THEIR INSIGNIFICANT TRAGEDIES ...

DO YOU CAUSE THEM? ...

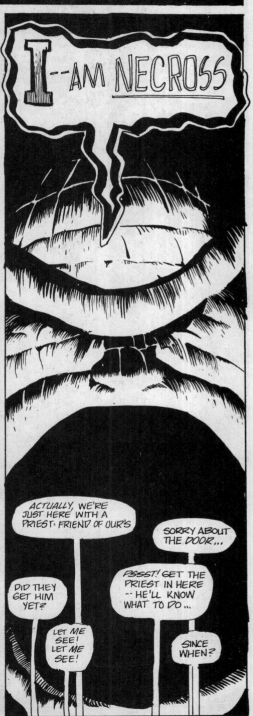

AND NOW PRIEST!

STOMP

AAAAAAAKKKKKK....

MORE THAN ANYTHING ELSE CEREBUS HATED ANY COUNTRY WHERE IT WAS IMPOSSIBLE FOR A THIEF/BARBARIAN/ SOLDIER TO MAKE A...

...LIVING?

SAY--CAN SOMEONE GET ME A DAMP BEDSHEET?

THE BOTTOMS OF MY FEET ARE KIND OF STICKY

ALL RIGHT WHERE DID EVERYBODY GO?

THIS IS THE ONLY REINFORCED FLOOR IN THE WHOLE TOWER! I'M *TRAPPED* IN HERE

I'M GOING TO COUNT **TEN** AND IF SOMEONE DOESN'T GET HERE...

...I'M IN **BIG TROUBLE!**

DAMN!

END

Introductions

"Silverspoon" (reprinted from the Buyer's Guide for Comic Fandom 1980 issues.)

"The Walls of Palnu" (Cerebus #14, March 1980)

"A Day in the Pits" (Cerebus #15, April 1980)

"A Night at the Masque" (Cerebus #16, May 1980)

Hokay.

As I said in the last introduction, I was getting very tired of doing commercial artwork for milk and bread money. Dreaming up snappy slogans like "Femme Fit Jeans - They fit your Femme." Perfect J.B. I think it'll play in Tilsonburg. So I started scouting around for people to sell Cerebus to as a regular feature. Which was when I thought of The Buyer's Guide, a comics ad newspaper with a large circulation. The way I figured it, I could sell a series of one-page strips to be published in TBG each week. I would make a few dollars, the book would have what amounted to a free full page ad in each issue of TBG and best of all it would be time for Dave Sim of Kitchener, Ontario to play "Hal Foster for a Day!"

Seriously now, regional prejudice and national pride aside, not even considering all the pros and cons of Neal Adam's style versus Alex Toth's, the high contrast use of black and white versus thin line realism versus impressionist styling versus stylish impressionism, when it comes down to three-quarters of an inch of steel and a piece of paper and some ink and making a thatched hut with rough-hewn wooden shutters look like a thatched hut with rough-hewn wooden shutters in four lines or less, give me Hal Foster in his prime. Of all the artists I tried to imitate (and if you think Barry Smith noodling drops off the end of the average pen, I have news for you.) Hal Foster is without a doubt, the single most difficult to nail down, for a very obvious reason. The-man-knew-how-to-draw. *Really* draw.

It is a testament to his sheer ability that so few people have attempted to imitate him and that the artists who have managed an *adequate* version of Hal Foster are outstanding by their rarity. Wally Wood's same *Prince Valiant* strip comes to mind - Jeff Jones *Valiant* parody I saw a few years back at a convention. By contrast Alex Raymond, one of Hal Foster's few peers in drawing ability was imitated by almost everyone in the fledgling comic book industry of the thirties and forties - slashing brush strokes for a background, sharp angular squinty features. Foster's style, as the ensuing eleven pages should demonstrate, is not as accessible. All superflous detail is eliminated. Every Foster drawing is like a well-designed vehicle. No wind resistance. Nothing there but what should be there. I mean, there are artists you can imitate by adding a pen stroke here, some cross-hatching there, some texturing on this bit. With Hal Foster you have four pen lines to get it right and then the buzzer goes and you lose the trip to Hawaii and the year's supply of taco chips. On the writing side, *Prince Valiant* has to be one of the oddest creatures going, past, present and future. On the one hand, it is an epic of awesome proportions - the closest in fact, to what I was attempting with Cerebus. Foster produced two thousand pages of Prince Valiant's life, starting when he's young, having him meet his future wife, lose her, find her again, get married, have kids, have the kids grow up and have adventures. Wanting my Val parody to be as authentic in it's literary form as possible, I read what pages I could get my hands on, hoping to find some "hook" for a parody.

It fairly lept from the page. Prince Valiant reads like an old issue of "Boy's Life" or "The Rover Boys go to College". There is implicit in the writing a sense that the Brits are just naturally superior to the Vikings, the Celts and any of those scruffy sorts who will come up to the gates, right up to the gates, mind you, without so much as a by your leave. Val prevails because he has good breeding, unshakable confidence, and a grander sense of purpose than these low-lifes.

Viewed from my own perverse vantage point ("Hey, you should see what Prince Valiant looks like from over here"), Prince Valiant becomes a pampered aristocrat, prevailing because he has more protein in his diet than any fifty Celts ("Jeeves, another pheasant"). A spoiled brat, unable to see his lofty position as anything but his birthright as a superior person. I just sort of stretched it a bit, really.

Hokay.

The time between Cerebus #13 and #14 was very interesting. I was right royally sick of doing commercial art (did I mention that, yet?) generally, and working for people who wouldn't know a marketable idea or effective drawing if they tripped over it, specifically. it was a rare bit of insight indeed, coming as it did on a clear, but icy cold January night. "Why not do the book monthly?"

I now knew for certain that I could draw twenty-two pages in a month's time - actually more like a month and a few days. I decided to cut the page count to twenty pages just to be on the safe side. I couldn't go to sleep that night . . . I thought I had died and gone to comicbook heaven. To never have to draw another newspaper ad, pair of jeans, cartoon mascot, soccer ball, Buy! Buy! Buy!, 30% OFF or SALE!.

I waxed enthusiastic to Deni about my idea and, of course, she was not crazy about it. She reminded me that less than a year before I had had a nervous breakdown, ostensibly, from overwork. She reminded me that I had just started doing weekly strips for the Buyer's Guide and how would I find the extra time to do *them*? I protested that I would just stop doing the strip. She reminded me that I couldn't stop the strip in mid-story, I argued that the strip was part of the continuity, and would stand as a suitable transition between issues 13 and 14 someday. I'll leave it to you to decide if it does.

But I'm getting ahead of myself.

I realized at the time that I started the Prince Valiant parody that the key to Silverspoon would be a father who would come to rescue him no matter what kind of trouble he got into. I had already selected Palnu, a city almost directly south of Iest, unimaginably wealthy by virtue of it's position between the Feldwar States (Upper and Lower Felda and Iest) and the Southern City States (Eshnosopur, Panrovy, etc.). I pictured it's ruler as the inventor of the Estarcion bureaucracy, a concept where you fight unemployment by giving everyone a government job (a concept near and dear to American Democratic and Republican presidents and Canadian Conservative and Liberal prime ministers). Of course the bureaucracy is in it's infant stages in Cerebus and consequently seems to solve the problem of the finite economy quite nicely, by making government it's own job-creation program. I also envisioned Palnu as a grand experiment in socialism and uniformity. Everyone would wear the same clothes, eat the same food, live in uniform dwellings and procede full speed ahead on whatever task the "Director of Trade" had set for them as a people. Basically this city was an Oligarchy gone strange. Heads of various families vied for the position of Grandlord and the most popular with his peers was the one who held the title . . . until he was no longer popular. I saw the present Director of Trade as a charismatic businessman in the midst of an old-boy aristocracy, consolidating his position with the people by capturing the lion's share of Estarcion's assets and distributing them like dividends to his citizens (I read a while ago that Alaska is doing the same thing with its windfall oil profits. No matter how bizarre I try to make the story, real life usually beats me to it). As the quintessential figure of the emerging merchant class, the Director of Trade would be concerned with running a profitable city. Palnu becomes the first import-export dominated culture to also manufacture consumer goods, mass-producing the tunics, trousers and boots everyone wears and exporting what they don't need to clothe their own people. The problem was that I kept picturing K'cor as the Grandlord. Someone big enough and strong enough to keep everyone in line and function as the absolute center of his city-state. All roads would lead to the Grandlord's office in Palnu's Trade Building.

It was not until Christmas of 1979 when Deni and I attended a ChristmasCon in Philadelphia (really) and we stayed with Howard Leroy Davis of the Delaware Valley Comics Consortium the night before that I figured it out. I had bought the latest Comic Journal at a Philadelphia comic shop that day and it contained the first major review of Cerebus by Kim (give me a "K") Thompson. You have to understand that this first review was critically important to me, because after two years, I had had almost no feedback from the major fan press, which led me to believe that either a) there was something seriously wrong with the book that led everyone but a couple of thousand loyal fans to dismiss it out of hand or b) no one really knew what to say about it besides "weird stuff".

One of the points Kim made was that (except for Red Sophia) most of the parodies I had done became, to him, solid characters in their own right - in effect, greater than the sum of their parts. This was immensely reassuring to me, since I had begun to think by the end of year two that potential reviewers were looking at the book and saying "Right. Elric, but he talks like Foghorn Leghorn. HaHaHa." I had avoided this kind of parody since introducing Elrod for fear that people would see it as an inability to concoct original material. After reading Kim's review (for the eighth time I think) I decided to see if I could apply an outside figure to the role of Grandlord and make him stick. Groucho came to mind almost immediately.

Small detour . . . . I introduced a friend of mine, Lyle Fisher, to Groucho in Grade 11. I'd rack my brain to remember Groucho lines from the Marx Brother's movies and every day, I'd nail Lyle with another one.

"We have to fight for this lady's honour, which is more than she ever did."

"Do you have milk-fed chickens? Well squeeze one and bring me a glass."

Lyle got into more trouble in Physics class

for laughing out loud while I was (ahem) just trying to finish writing up the last experiment. Strangely enough, the only other lines that would crack Lyle up would be Foghorn Leghorn lines.

"It's a trunk son! Big suitcase, that is!"

The impact of these characters wasn't lost on me, I guess, and it is natural that they would end up in Cerebus.

The interesting thing about Groucho is that, like John Wayne, he came to *be* the person he *portrayed*. A kind of integration of character and the man took place over the years. I should think that was why he was so pleased when a Los Angeles television station started showing the old "You Bet Your Life" show and that it garnered a wide following in a short time. "You Bet Your Life" was Groucho the Natural Wit, improvising repartee with Joe and Mary Average, proving week after week that it wasn't just great writers that made the Groucho character tick. Groucho was Groucho. I doubt that many people realized before then Groucho's flair for improvising the kind of dialogue he dispensed in the Marx Brothers' movies. It was this quality of verbal manipulation and control that became the essence of Lord Julius (Julius Marx is Groucho's real name). Like Rufus T. Firefly, the head of state for Freedonia in the Marx Brothers' "Duck Soup", one senses Lord Julius stumbling from one calamity to another, his nimble wits and the lack of sense of humour on the part of his underlings, giving him the advantage in most situation. The major strength of the Groucho character is his imperturbability and his refusal to be cornered on any point of contention. "Whatever it is, I'm against it!" Firefly sings to the assembled people of Freedonia. Sung to a bureaucracy, you could keep a thousand lawyers employed full-time trying to find a way around the purity of the nonsense.

"Baskin, my boy, come in. Whatever it is, I'm against it."

"Lord Julius?"

"Unless of course, I'm for it, in which case the tie goes to the runner."

"It's the papers you asked to see on the shipment to Eshnosopur."

Lord Julius' position affords nothing but options. If he says he doesn't remember that shipment, his underlings dutifully relay that message, throwing whoever they relayed it to into confusion and near panic.

"Gak! Doesn't remember? I told you! It's a set-up! A trick!"

One pictures Groucho as welcome replacement for Ronald in the Oval Office.

"Casper, my boy, come in. I want to talk to you about Argentina."

"What about Argentina?"

"Funny. That's just what Margaret Thatcher said."

Suffice it to say that after two years of writing Lord Julius, I am continually amazed at the very basic comedic richness of the character Julius Marx developed for the world at large to enjoy. I try to remain as faithful to it as I can, and I look forward to aging him in the book as the world saw him age . . . the eternal anarchist, caustic, brilliant, insufferable, maddening, and hilarious at the same time. I think every civilization needs their Julius Marx. Palnu is just fortunate enough to have theirs running the whole show.

I remembered while reading the three Palnu issues what an immense task I had set for myself doing what was essentially a sixty-page story. At the time I tended not to see the book in terms of being one very long continuity. I was striving to hold to a reasonably fixed view of Estarcion, chafing at the constraints that course imposed. Many was the time I would be tempted to go ahead with a bit of funny business that contradicted the major continuity I was forming in my head. I appreciate the effort more in retrospect than I did at the time and I'm often surprised at some slightly twisted turn of phrase that hints at concepts I've begun to develop more fully in the last year or so. This was definitely the point where my awareness of Estarcion as a major fixture . . . almost a central character . . . in the story began to develop even more rapidly. I still have maps that my brother-in-law Michael had drawn up of the geography and cartography of Estarcion. Where possible I try to adhere to them and I have amplified them a great deal in the last few years.

One major worry of mine at the time, and one which I remembered again while re-reading these issues was the wall-to-wall cliches. "The revolution-ary mystic cult" - "the ruins of the city beneath the city" - "the duel on the bridge", and of course, the grandaddy of them all, "the battle with the Giant Snake". Okay, I was doing a parody, but ho-hum, y'know? You can run out of the "twenty-eight Deadly Fantasy Cliches" (or however many there are) after a dozen issues if your character gets around enough. "The Giant Snake" was a must, though, for this reason; I couldn't wait to write this introduction . You know why? So I could tell E*V*E*R*Y*O*N*E that yes, I was thinking of the phallic symbolism the whole time I was drawing the snake. It's true. The whole time I was drawing the snake I was thinking "This isn't a snake I'm drawing, I'm drawing a Giant Dick with eyes", or "I'm not drawing a snake crawling out of his cage with the leader of the 'Eye in the Pyramid' juxtaposed in the foreground. Hell, no! I'm drawing the leader of the 'Eye in the Pyramid' flipping his giant schlong out at Cerebus, who's going to cut it off." Why do you think those torches on the wall are at a forty-five degree angle? That's right! They're really all stiff wee-wees with their tips on fire (ouch). Right down to the big "O" scene where the giant "snake" smashes into the wall and behind it to the Leader of the 'Eye in the Pyramid'. Sort of changes the meaning of the "AAAAH" word balloon doesn't it? Now, why, you might very well ask yourself, why would someone consciously sit down and draw an allegory that revolves around a huge male member. Someday, folks, I hope to open the Underground Comix Price Guide, flip to the appendix with Cerebus and read:

Cerebus   Good   Fine   Mint

#15 (Giant penis issue)

$20 $30 $40

And people say I've lost my ambition.

Ladies and gentlemen . . . my first 71 page Cerebus story . . .

(NOTE - this introduction was written before Hal Foster's recent death. I apologize for the irreverent tone of parts of it; the decision to leave it in that form was mine. I hope no one takes offence.)

Cerebus THE AARDVARK

SYNOPSIS: HAVING DECIDED TO LEAVE LOWER FELDA BEHIND, CEREBUS MAKES HIS WAY TO THE PORT CITY OF DENIEALI, WHERE HE BOOKS PASSAGE...

ON THE TRADING VESSEL *CUTTER* BOUND FOR HOME -- THE CITY-STATE OF PALNU

"IT IS A RARE SUMMER'S DAY" CRIED THE SICKENINGLY CHEERFUL SON OF THE DIRECTOR OF TRADE AT PALNU.

"IT HAS THE SMELL OF NEW ADVENTURE TO IT" SMILES YOUNG LORD SILVERSPOON TURNING HIS FACE TO THE SUN

"AND A HOLD FILLED WITH WINE AND SPICES" HE CHUCKLES. "FATHER WILL BE SO PROUD!"

"BUT *NOW*, WE SET SAIL FOR THE *BAY OF SUNSHEE* -- AND WHO KNOWS WHAT PIRATES AND BRIGANDS WE SHALL ENCOUNTER IN OUR TRAVELS?" HE BUBBLES FLINGING OUT HIS ARM, CARELESSLY.

"SURE THING" MUTTERS THE EARTH-PIG "HOW ABOUT A SEA SERPENT WHILE WE'RE THERE, YOU SNOTTY ARISTOCRATIC BRAT"

DAVE SIM

NEXT WEEK: SEA SERPENT

Cerebus THE AARDVARK

"GREAT TARIM" CRIES THE CREW IN UNISON, "IT IS A SEA SERPENT!"

"ONE SIDE, EARTH-PIG" CRIES SILVER-SPOON, "THIS IS MY SPECIALTY"

"SOMEONE HELP ME GET THE ROWBOAT INTO THE WATER," HE ADDS, "AND BRING ME A SWORD"

#2

"WHAT ON EARTH IS THAT THING" QUERIES CEREBUS. "IT'S MOSTLY MADE OF ANIMAL FAT AND PLASTER AND SNAKE SKIN," ANSWERS DHUFU, ONE OF THE MERCHANTS "WE MAKE A HABIT OF DROPPING IT INTO THE WATER AT LEAST ONCE PER VOYAGE, SO THAT HIS LORDSHIP HAS THE ADVENTURE HE SEEKS"
"BUT ISN'T THIS A RATHER TIME-CONSUMING WAY TO HUMOUR HIM?" ASKS THE EARTH-PIG, AS SILVERSPOON HACKS A LARGE PIECE OUT OF THE 'SERPENT.'
"POSSIBLY, BUT IT'S EASIER TO LIVE WITH THAN HIS LORDSHIP'S OTHER INTEREST."
"WHICH IS WHAT?"

"ENGAGING ONLIU PIRATE VESSELS IN EXTENDED NAVAL BATTLES AND FIGHTING TO THE LAST MAN" COMES THE REPLY.'

DAVE SIM

"YES," AGREED CEREBUS "I CAN SEE HOW THIS IS A LESS DANGEROUS HOBBY FOR A YOUNG NOBLE"

NEXT WEEK: ONLIU PIRATE VESSEL

Cerebus THE AARDVARK

SYNOPSIS: WITH BARELY A HALF DOZEN ARMED SOLDIERS, CEREBUS DIRECTS THE DEFENCE OF THE TRADING VESSEL CUTTER, UNDER ATTACK FROM ONLIU PIRATES.

ABRUPTLY, "THEY HAVE A CATAPULT! FIREBALLS COMING THIS WAY--"

THE ARROWS, HOWEVER, CONTINUE TO FALL FAR SHORT OF THEIR INTENDED TARGET

"ABANDON SHIP" BELLOWS THE AARDVARK--"GRAB ALL NECESSARY PROVISIONS"

"I CAN'T BLOW THEM OUT FROM UP HERE! KEEP FIRING," SNARLS THE EARTH-PIG.

#3

AND, INSIDE OF AN HOUR, A MAKESHIFT BUCKET BRIGADE FIGHTS A LOSING BATTLE AGAINST THE INFERNO RAGING AMIDSHIPS

DAVE SIM

"YOU HEARD HIM," WHINES SILVERSPOON "SOMEONE GET MY CASE OF CHATEAU DEHRSION '26"

NEXT WEEK: **SHIPWRECKED**

Cerebus THE AARDVARK

CEREBUS WATCHES AS THE *CUTTER* SINKS BENEATH THE WAVES, BILLOWING STEAM MINGLING WITH OILY, BLACK SMOKE AS THE TRADE SHIP VANISHES FROM SIGHT. THOUGH HE LOOKS CAREFULLY FOR IT, THERE IS NO SIGN OF THE ONLIU PIRATE SHIP.

#4

THE CREW, ELECTING TO ATTEMPT THE LONG VOYAGE TO PALNU IN OPEN BOATS, HAS TURNED WEST...

FEELING THE RISK TO BE TOO GREAT, CEREBUS CHOOSES A SMALL SUB-TROPICAL ISLAND AS HIS IMMEDIATE DESTINATION.

THOUGH UNSURE OF HIS OWN PLANS HE IS AT LEAST *GRATEFUL* TO BE RID OF THE ARROGANT AND INSUFFERABLE YOUNG SILVERSPOON

DOUBTLESS, HE HAS JOINED THE *CUTTER* IN ITS WATERY GRAVE. CEREBUS COULD PICTURE HIM, CLINGING TENACIOUSLY TO HIS WINE AND SPICE CRATES...

"WELL, IT'S ABOUT TIME SOMEONE *SHOWED UP!*" COMES THE FAMILIAR NASAL WHINE. "*I* WAS BEGINNING TO THINK I WOULD HAVE TO GO FORAGING FOR MY OWN FOOD, FOR HEAVEN'S SAKE!"

DAVE SIM

NEXT: DIVISION OF LABOUR

Cerebus THE AARDVARK

"IF YOU THINK I INTEND TO FORAGE FOR YOUR MEALS AS WELL AS MY OWN," SNARLS THE EARTH-PIG.

SILVERSPOON CUTS HIM OFF. "NATURALLY MY FATHER WILL PAY YOU WHEN WE REACH PALNU··SHALL WE SAY A HUNDRED GOLD PIECES?"

"TWO HUNDRED!" SNAPS CEREBUS. "AGREED," SMILES SILVERSPOON.

AS HE MOVES OFF IN SEARCH OF SUSTENANCE, CEREBUS WONDERS IF HE HAS WON THE ARGUMENT --OR LOST IT.

A NORTHERNER SINCE BIRTH, CEREBUS SOON FINDS FORAGING A MORE DIFFICULT TASK THAN HE HAD EXPECTED.

HE COULD SEPARATE THE POISONOUS FROM THE EDIBLE BASED ON SHADES OF GREEN AND BROWN, BUT WAS STYMIED BY THE RAINBOW COLOURED VEGETATION

"AT LEAST" MUTTERS THE EARTH-PIG TO HIMSELF "THAT EXPLAINS WHY HUMANS NEVER SETTLED ON THIS ISLAND."

NEXT: NATIVES

CEREBUS THE AARDVARK #13 IS AVAILABLE FROM SEA-GATE DISTRIBUTORS, BOX 177, CONEY ISLAND STN., BROOKLYN, N.Y. 11224, BUD PLANT, BOX 1886, GRASS VALLEY, CALIFORNIA, 95945 AND NOW & THEN BOOKS, 103 QUEEN ST. S., KITCHENER, ONTARIO -- ONE DOLLAR AND .25 POSTAGE

Cerebus THE AARDVARK

SYNOPSIS: IN EXCHANGE FOR TWO HUNDRED GOLD PIECES PROMISED HIM BY THE YOUNG LORD SILVERSPOON, CEREBUS HAS GONE FORAGING FOR THEIR EVENING MEAL. HIS QUEST IS INTERRUPTED BY TWO ARMED NATIVES

"FROM WHAT I GATHER, THEY WANT US TO GO WITH THEM TO THEIR VILLAGE," SAYS THE EARTH-PIG.

"TELL THEM WE'LL BRING OUT THE BEADS AND THE TRINKETS AFTER WE'VE EATEN," SAYS SILVERSPOON, WAVING OFF THE INTERRUPTION.

"I DON'T THINK THEY WANT TO WAIT THAT LONG," SAYS CEREBUS, RAISING HIS VOICE SLIGHTLY.

"OH, PIFFLE, YOU'RE NOT GOING TO LET THESE IGNORANT SAVAGES PUSH YOU AROUND ARE YOU?" ASKS SILVERSPOON, "TELL THEM TO SHOO!"

"CRAK!" SAYS A ROCK AND SILVERSPOON'S FOREHEAD IN UNISON.

#6   DAVE SIM

"NOW WHY DIDN'T I THINK OF THAT?" PONDERS CEREBUS ALOUD.

NEXT: FUN AND GAMES

Cerebus THE AARDVARK

SILVERSPOON RETURNS TO CONSCIOUSNESS OVER A PERIOD OF SEVERAL MINUTES, AT LAST RECOGNIZING THE BUZZING IN HIS EARS AS CEREBUS' VOICE. "WE'VE BEEN TAKEN CAPTIVE, BRAT," GROWLS THE EARTH-PIG. "TRY NOT TO MAKE THEM ANY ANGRIER, OKAY."

"RAGGA RAGGA NUMU LUM TUM DIDDY YAH-YAH," SUGGESTS ONE OF THE NATIVES.

"UM TUT SUT LIM LUM BUBBA BUB BUBA BOO," DISAGREES HIS COMPANION.

"SHA-BOOM SHA-BOOM," OPINES A THIRD MEMBER OF THE GROUP.

"WHAT ARE THEY SAYING?" ASKS SILVERSPOON. "THEY'RE BETTING ON WHAT WILL GET US FIRST — EXPOSURE OR STARVATION," ANSWERS CEREBUS.

NEXT: A STICKY WICKET

Cerebus THE AARDVARK

SYNOPSIS: CEREBUS AND SILVERSPOON HAVE BEEN TAKEN CAPTIVE BY NATIVES WHO HAVE TIED THEM SIDE-BY-SIDE IN THE OPEN. THE TEMPERATURE SOARS EACH DAY AS THE SUN MAKES ITS INFINITELY SLOW CIRCUIT ACROSS THE SKY.

#8

LATE EVENING BRINGS THE POUNDING OF MIDSUMMER RAINS, DRENCHING THE LANDSCAPE AS THE SUN SINKS FROM VIEW.

THEN, THE LONG HOURS OF NIGHT AND NEAR-FREEZING TEMPERATURES UNDER A STAR-FILLED SKY...

AS THE SUN BEGINS ITS RISE ONCE MORE INSECTS FEED ON HUMAN AND AARDVARK FLESH...

FOUR DAYS! CEREBUS WAS USED TO SUCH HARSH CONDITIONS BUT WHAT OF THE CITY-BRED BRAT? HOW LONG COULD HE LAST?

DAVE SIM

"CHATEAU DEHRSION '26," GASPS YOUNG SILVERSPOON, FROM BETWEEN PARCHED LIPS, "CHATEAU DEHRSION '26."

"HE MAY BE ON THE VERGE OF DEATH," MUSES CEREBUS "BUT HIS BREEDING IS IMPECCABLE."

NEXT: DADDY

Cerebus THE AARDVARK

OUR STORY: CEREBUS WAKES TO THE SOUND OF SPLINTERING BAMBOO. ARMED SOLDIERS ARE BREAKING INTO THE SMALL VILLAGE, THE BRONZE-SKINNED NATIVES DROPPING LIKE FLIES IN THE FACE OF SWORDS AND CROSSBOWS. "HEY, BRAT," GRUMBLES THE EARTH-PIG, "VISITORS." "DADDY" CRIES SILVERSPOON, HIS EYES SHINING WITH DELIGHT.

"DADDY?" QUERIES THE EARTH-PIG. "OF COURSE, SILLY" REPLIES THE YOUNG HEIR, "IT'S DADDY AND HIS TROOPS COME TO RESCUE ME."

"OVER HERE, DADDY," CRIES SILVERSPOON. CEREBUS CAN HARDLY BELIEVE HIS GOOD LUCK! SOON HE WOULD BE RID OF THE BRAT AND HAVE HIS REWARD FOR SAVING THE BOY'S LIFE.

DAVE SIM

"HE'LL PROBABLY KILL YOU WHEN I TELL HIM HOW YOU KIDNAPPED ME" INTONES SILVERSPOON AS A SLENDER MAN APPROACHES...

NEXT: OUT OF THE FRYING PAN

Cerebus THE AARDVARK

#10

OUR STORY: SILVERSPOON'S FATHER ARRIVES WITH ARMED SOLDIERS TO RESCUE THE YOUNG HEIR. AS HIS BONDS ARE SEVERED, HE RELATES A GRIM (AND ENTIRELY FICTITIOUS) TALE OF HIS KIDNAPPING BY CEREBUS THE AARDVARK.

"HE REALLY DID, DADDY, I PROMISE. REALLY! LET ME EXECUTE HIM, PLEASE! PLEASE! I HAVEN'T EXECUTED ANYONE IN WEEKS." WHINES YOUNG SILVERSPOON.

DAVE SIM

"UH -- HOW ABOUT IF WE WAIT UNTIL THIS LITTLE SITUATION IS ALL CLEARED UP BEFORE WE..."

"NO NO NO!" SHRIEKS SILVERSPOON STAMPING AN ARISTOCRATIC BOOT ON THE GROUND. "YOU'RE JUST STALLING! YOU NEVER LET ME HAVE ANY FUN ANYMORE! IT'S NOT FAIR! IT'S NOT FAIR! IT'S NOT..."

"NICE THROWING" SAYS LORD JULIUS TO ONE OF HIS MEN. "GLXXP" SAYS SILVERSPOON JUST BEFORE LAPSING INTO UNCONSCIOUSNESS.

NEXT: PEACE and QUIET

Cerebus THE AARDVARK

#11

OUR STORY: CEREBUS WATCHES AS SILVERSPOON IS LOADED ABOARD THE SHIP SOON TO BE BOUND FOR PALNU. HIS FATHER, LORD JULIUS, HAS OFFERED TO GIVE CEREBUS FREE PASSAGE ON THE VESSEL AND PROMISES THAT A REWARD AWAITS THE EARTH-PIG WHEN THEY REACH PORT. "WHAT WILL HAPPEN TO THE BR... UH... SILVERSPOON WHEN HE WAKES UP," ASKS CEREBUS.

"I HADN'T REALLY THOUGHT ABOUT IT," ADMITS LORD JULIUS, "I SUPPOSE I'LL SEND HIM TO A BOY'S MILITARY SCHOOL..."

"BUT SILVERSPOON HAS TRAVELLED THE WORLD," VENTURES CEREBUS "WON'T A BOY'S SCHOOL BE A LITTLE BIT... WELL... BORING?"

DAVE SIM

"YOU KNOW, YOU'RE RIGHT," AGREES JULIUS -- "MAYBE I'LL SEND HIM TO A GIRL'S SCHOOL INSTEAD..."

NEXT: A NEW ADVENTURE

SYNOPSIS: AFTER LEAVING LOWER FELDA, CEREBUS BOARDS A TRADING VESSEL BOUND FOR PALNU! WHEN THE SHIP IS WAYLAID BY ONLIU PIRATES, CEREBUS AND THE SON OF THE DIRECTOR OF TRADE (AND ELECTED RULER) OF PALNU ARE SHIPWRECKED ON A DESERT ISLAND! RESCUED BY THE BOY'S FATHER AND HIS TROOPS, CEREBUS IS PROMISED A REWARD FOR SAVING THE YOUNG HEIR'S LIFE! THREE WEEKS LATER, THEY ARRIVE IN PALNU TO A TUMULTUOUS HERO'S WELCOME...

THE WALLS OF
Palnu

CEREBUS' EARS STILL RING WITH THE CRIES OF THE CROWDED STREETS AS HE SETTLES INTO JULIUS' OFFICE...

I'LL COME STRAIGHT TO THE POINT! AS A REWARD FOR SAVING MY SON'S LIFE, I'D LIKE YOU TO BE IN CHARGE OF MY SECURITY FORCES...

YOUR OFFICIAL TITLE WILL BE "KITCHEN STAFF SUPERVISOR"

WHY NOT "DIRECTOR OF SECURITY FORCES"?

IMPOSSIBLE--THAT'S THE TITLE I GAVE TO THE SECRETARY OF THE NAVY...

BUT, IF HE'S THE SEC-RETARY OF THE NAVY, WHY DID YOU GIVE HIM ...?

WHEN YOU'RE RUNNING A BUREAUCRACY, THE BEST WAY TO SAFE-GUARD YOUR JOB IS TO MAKE SURE YOU'RE THE ONLY ONE WHO KNOWS HOW THE WHOLE THING WORKS...

SO WHAT DOES THE SECRETARY OF THE NAVY DO?

HE MEETS TWICE A WEEK WITH THE COOK TO PLAN MILITARY STRATEGY

AND WHAT IS CEREBUS SUPPOSED TO DO?

AS I SAID, YOU'LL BE IN CHARGE OF MY SECURITY FORCES! YOU'LL MAKE SURE THAT NO ONE ASSASSINATES ME ...

IF THEY DO, YOU'RE FIRED.

HOW MANY MEN WOULD CEREBUS HAVE AS... KITCHEN STAFF SUPERVISOR?

HOW MANY *MEN*?!

I GIVE YOU A POSITION HALF OF PALNU WOULD KILL THEIR *GRANDMOTHERS* FOR AND YOU WANT *MEN* AS WELL...?

I'M NOT AS STUPID AS I *LOOK*, MY BOY! SUPPOSE I PUT YOU IN CHARGE OF *FIVE* MEN? SOON, IT'LL BE SIX... THEN *TEN!* INSIDE OF SIX MONTHS, YOU'LL BE COMMANDING MORE MANPOWER THAN THE SENIOR AIDE TO THE FILE CLERK!

AND A FINE KETTLE OF FISH *THAT* WOULD BE!

OH NO! I CATCH YOU EMPLOYING EVEN ONE FREELANCE SPY AND I'LL HAVE YOU REDUCED TO *EXECUTIVE SECRETARY OF THE INTERIOR* SO FAST YOU WON'T REMEMBER WHAT A KITCHEN LOOKS LIKE...

CEREBUS FINDS THIS *VERY* CONFUSING...

LORD JULIUS THE REPRESENTATIVES OF THE SATELLITE CITIES OF PARMOC, CIHNU, AVERS, ENIATH AND JYLCEW AWAIT YOUR BIDDING...

I WOULDN'T BID A HALF-PIECE FOR THE *LOT*, BUT SHOW THEM IN, ANYHOW...

VERY GOOD, M'LORD!

MOMENTS LATER...

GENTLEMEN--AND I USE THE TERM ADVISEDLY--SINCE IT TOOK FOUR HOURS TO FUMIGATE AFTER YOUR LAST VISIT, I'LL MAKE THIS SHORT AND SWEET...

I AM ASKING EACH OF YOU TO PROVIDE A FORCE OF ONE THOUSAND FIGHTING MEN TO ASSIST IN REPELLING ONLIU'S ANNUAL ASSAULT ON OUR FAIR BORDERS...

IMPOSSIBLE

UNREASONABLE

OUT OF THE QUESTION

IF YOU REFUSE, I'LL HAVE NO CHOICE BUT TO CALL UPON YOUR INTIMATE KNOWLEDGE OF THE SITUATION AND PRESS YOU INTO SERVICE AS FRONTLINE MILITARY ADVISORS...

PATRIOTISM KNOWS NO LIMITATIONS!

NATURALLY, PARMOC WILL DO ITS BEST!

IS A FORTNIGHT TOO SOON?

THANK YOU GENTLEMEN...

NOW, WHERE WERE WE?

DON'T SLAM IT ON YOUR WAY OUT

CEREBUS WAS ABOUT TO ASK-- WHAT'S IN THIS DEAL FOR HIM?

AMAZING! SIMPLY AMAZING!

YOU'VE ONLY BEEN IN THE CITY TWO HOURS AND ALREADY YOU SOUND LIKE A NATIVE...

YOU'LL BE GIVEN YOUR OWN ROOM HERE IN THE TRADE BUILDING, ALL THE FOOD, WINE AND ALE YOU CAN CONSUME AND MORE SPARE TIME THAN YOU'LL KNOW HOW TO HANDLE...

AND IF YOU HAVE ANY QUESTIONS, ASK SOMEONE ELSE! THERE'S A RUMOUR GOING AROUND THAT I'M VERY BUSY RIGHT NOW.

FOLLOW ME, SIR. I WILL SHOW YOU TO YOUR ROOM.

CEREBUS HAD NEVER BEEN TO PALNU, BUT, IN THE COURSE OF HIS TRAVELS, HAD HEARD MUCH A- BOUT IT! MOST OUTLANDERS DWELT AT SOME LENGTH ON ITS SIZE AND WEALTH! SINCE HE HAD DECIDED TO REMAIN HERE, HE WOULD NEED TO KNOW MORE.! THERE WAS AN EXPRES- SION IN SERREA; "WHEN THE DRUNKARD SPEAKS THE SOBER MAN LEARNS MUCH." WITHIN THE HOUR, CEREBUS HAD LOCATED A SUITABLE BUREAUCRAT AT THE "FROG AND DUCK" AND, FOR THE PRICE OF A FEW TANKARDS, IS SOON UP TO HIS MEDALLIONS IN INFORMATION.

THE ARISTOCRACY HAD ALL BUT VANISHED IN PALNU! BOUND AS THEY WERE TO THEIR ENORMOUS ESTATES, THEY WERE NO COM- PETITION FOR THE THRIVING MERCHANT CLASS WHOSE ASSETS NOW GENERATED UNDREAMT- OF INCOME. THERE WERE FIVE DOMINANT MERCHANT "HOUSES" WITHIN THE CITY WALLS. THESE HOUSES EMPLOYED "CLIENTS," EACH CITIZEN OF VOTING AGE BEING A CLIENT, THEIR LIVING EXPENSES PAID BY THE HOUSE "LORD" IN EXCHANGE FOR THEIR VOTE.' THE LORD' BY PAYING FOR THESE VOTES, ASSURED HIMSELF OF A PLACE ON THE "GRAND COUNCIL OF PALNU." THE LORD WHO OWNED THE MOST CLIENTS, AND HENCE, VOTES WAS MADE 'GRANDLORD' OF THE CITY AND ITS SURROUNDING TERRITORY.' AT THE MOMENT, THIS WAS LORD JULIUS.' THE WRINKLE THAT JULIUS HAD ADDED TO THIS IDEA WAS THE SELLING OF TITLES FOR ADDITIONAL REVENUE.' THE LORDS OF THE NOUVEAU- RICHE MERCHANT HOUSES, HAVING, SOME TIME BEFORE, RUN OUT OF THINGS TO BUY, NOW FILLED JULIUS' COFFERS IN EXCHANGE FOR THE TITLE OF THEIR CHOICE! THESE THEY HANDED OUT LIKE PARTY FAVOURS TO CONCUBINES, FAMILY BODYGUARDS, ACCOUNTANTS, NIECES, NEPHEWS AND, OF COURSE, THEMSELVES. JULIUS HIMSELF WAS GRANDLORD SUPREME, BARON OF THE HOUSE OF TAVERS, RIGHT HONOURABLE PRIME MINISTER OF PALNU, PRESIDENT OF PARMOC, COUNT OF CIHNU...

THERE WERE A NUMBER OF OTHER TITLES HE HAD PAID FOR BUT CEREBUS HAD FORGOTTEN ANOTHER SERREAN EXPRESSION;

"WHEN THE BUREAUCRAT SPEAKS, THE SOUND OF SNORING SOON FILLS THE ROOM."

GENTLEMEN OF THE HOUSE OF TAVERS -- WE ARE HERE TODAY TO DISCUSS A GRAVE AND PRESSING SITUATION... I AM, OF COURSE, REFERRING TO THE CINNAMON CRISIS! THERE ARE THOSE AMONG YOU WHO ASK "WHAT CINNAMON CRISIS?"

OUR SUPPLY OF CINNAMON FROM THE ESHTANNIN WILDERNESS HAS BEEN DRASTICALLY CURTAILED BY COWARDLY ONLIU NAVAL ATTACKS! THERE IS EVERY INDICATION THAT BY LATE FALL, WE WILL BE COMPLETELY AND IRREVOCABLY CINNAMON-LESS...

IF I WAIT 'TIL HE'S THROUGH, I'LL STARVE!

THERE ARE THOSE AMONG YOU ASK "SO OUR BELOVED LEADER CAN'T HAVE CINNAMON TOAST WITH HIS HOT CHOCOLATE BEFORE BEDTIME -- WHY CAN'T HE BE A MAN ABOUT IT AND DO WITHOUT?"

MAYBE JUST ONE BITE.

THERE ARE PROBABLY THOSE AMONG YOU WHO SAY AS...

EEEEER

WELL -- THAT WASN'T IN THE SPEECH, BUT IT'S NOT A BAD ATTENTION-GETTER.

LORD JULIUS -- THIS FOOD IS POISONED!

THAT'S FUNNY -- I'VE BEEN SAYING THE SAME THING FOR YEARS...

THERE'S ONLY ONE THING TO DO -- EXECUTE THE COOK...

BUT, THE COOK MAY BE INNOCENT!

YOU'VE OBVIOUSLY NEVER HAD TO EAT ONE OF HIS *STUFFED TOMATOES!*

THE ASSASSIN HAD MADE A FATAL ERROR IN HIS ATTEMPT ON JULIUS' LIFE... THE POISON WAS EXOTIC FOR THIS PART OF THE WORLD, BUT CEREBUS HAD RECOGNIZED IT INSTANTLY! A FEW INQUIRIES LED HIM TO A NEARBY SHOP...

CLEPS
IMPORTS AND EXPORTS

GOOD MORROW -- A SHIPMENT HAS JUST ARRIVED FROM *ESHNOSOPUR?*

OOH -- YES! YES *INDEED!*

A *FINE* YEAR FOR WHEAT -- IT WILL MAKE A LOAF FIT FOR THE *GODS!*

CEREBUS WAS THINKING MORE OF A VIAL OF *PENTAZIN...*

A *TOXIN* NATIVE TO THAT COASTAL CITY...

I BUY ONLY WHEAT FROM *ESHNOSOPUR!* I'M AFRAID YOU'LL HAVE TO TRY....

IT WAS QUITE FASHIONABLE A FEW YEARS AGO... ADDED TO -- SAY -- A BIT OF POULTRY IT WAS FLAVOUR-LESS, BUT VERY SWIFT IN ITS...

CEREBUS CURSED HIMSELF FOR A PANKROVIAN... HE HAD UNDERESTIMATED THE EFFECT HIS ACCUSATION WOULD HAVE ON QIEPIE. THE MAN KNEW NOW THAT HE WAS BEING HUNTED AS A TRAITOR...

THOUGH A MERE HANDFUL OF SECONDS HAD ELAPSED...

ALREADY THE STREET HAD SWALLOWED UP HIS CORPULENT QUARRY...

AN HOUR LATER...

ONE OF MY IMPORTERS -- AN ASSASSIN?

SEND FOR THE ARMY!

WAIT!

LORD JULIUS -- THESE MATTERS ARE BEST HANDLED QUIETLY...!

SEND FOR THE ARMY AND HAVE THEIR FEET WRAPPED IN COTTON!!

WAIT! A LARGE FORCE WILL JUST DRIVE HIM UNDERGROUND! CEREBUS WILL INVESTIGATE ALONE!

THIS MAY NOT BE A *RANDOM* ATTEMPT ON YOUR LIFE...

YOUR ENEMIES MAY BE *ORGANIZED*...!

THAT WOULD PUT THEM A JUMP AHEAD OF MY *ARMY*, ALL RIGHT!

VERY WELL, MY POINTY-EARED FRIEND-- I'LL GIVE YOU A CHANCE...

BUT, REMEMBER THE WORDS OF NEAFON THE GREAT WHO ONCE SAID "IF AT FIRST YOU DON'T *SUCCEED*"...

"YOU BETTER START LOOKING FOR A NEW EMPLOYER..."

IT HAS BEEN THREE DAYS AND STILL NO SIGN OF GIEPIE! CEREBUS WAS CONVINCED THAT THE IMPORTER WOULD NOT LEAVE HIS POSSESSIONS UNGUARDED MUCH LONGER!

AN ODD SHIFTING OF SHADOWS IN THE ALLEYWAY OPPOSITE HIM ATTRACTS THE EARTH-PIG'S ATTENTION

IT IS THE FIGURE OF A MAN MOVING VERY CAUTIOUSLY TOWARD THE FRONT DOOR OF THE IMPORT SHOP.

IT WOULD APPEAR THAT CEREBUS' SUSPICIONS THAT GIEPE ISN'T IN THIS ALONE WERE *WELL-FOUNDED...*

THIRTY SECONDS TO FIND WHAT YOU SOUGHT AND PACK IT IN A VALISE...

CEREBUS IS NOT SO MUCH INTERESTED IN *WHAT* YOU ARE CARRYING AS HE IS ...

IN *WHO* YOU PLAN TO DELIVER IT TO!

CLOVIS' BURIAL MOUND! THIS IS THE TRADE BUILDING! IS IT POSSIBLE THAT JULIUS SENT FOR GIEPIE'S BELONGINGS?

THAT IDIOT! HE'LL RUIN ALL OF CEREBUS'...

HUH?

NOK NOK

NOK NOK NOK

ENTER! THE MEETING IS ABOUT TO BEGIN!

MEETING?

NOK
NOK

NOK
NOK
NOK

ENTER! THE MEETING IS ABOUT...

UGH

GUARD THAT MAN AND GET READY TO TAKE SOME PRISONERS!

AYE, SIR!

TO THE STAIRWAY! WE ARE BETRAYED! JULIUS' TROOPS APPROACH!

THE STAIRWAY!

ALL IS LOST!!

TARIM PRESERVE US!

QUICKLY!

GET AWAY!

AMID THE POUNDING OF RUNNING FEET, CEREBUS HEARS THE UNMISTAKABLE RASP...

..OF A SLIDING PANEL OF WOOD!

THE MECHANISM WAS NEVER INTENDED FOR ANYTHING MORE STRENUOUS THAN CONCEALMENT...

IT RESISTS, HUMMING ANGRILY, FOR A MOMENT! IN THE NEXT INSTANT, HOWEVER...

...AARDVARKIAN MUSCLES PREVAIL!

I AM CEREBUS, THE KITCHEN STAFF SUPERVISOR -- HALT IN THE NAME OF LORD JULIUS...

THERE'S NOWHERE TO RUN!

THE CHASE CONTINUES UP THREE FLIGHTS OF DARKENED STAIRS LEADING, FINALLY TO AN OPEN WINDOW! WAS IT POSSIBLE THE MAN HAD JUMPED?

JOIN US! -- THE REVOLUTION HAS NEED OF TRUE *PATRIOTS* WHO WISH TO RESTORE PALNU TO HER FORMER GREATNESS!

YOUR PLEAS FALL ON DEAF EARS, *STRIPLING!*

CEREBUS HAS A JOB TO DO -- NO MORE AND NO LESS! IF THE PRICE WAS RIGHT, HE WOULD FOLLOW A WOOD FAERIE IN A RELIGIOUS CRUSADE AGAINST THE ONLIU...

THE LEADER YOU FOLLOW -- THE LEADER WHOSE *GOLD* YOU ACCEPT SO *WILLINGLY*...

HOW'D YOU BOYS LIKE TO GO PLAY SOMEWHERE *ELSE* -- I HAVE SOME TRADE AGREEMENTS THAT I HAVE TO...

OH! IT'S *YOU!*

TELL ME -- HOW'S EVERY LITTLE THING IN THE KITCHEN?

CEREBUS HAS FOUND YOUR ASSASSIN...

WELL, WELL, WELL SO YOU HAVE

I'D ASK YOU BOTH IN FOR A DRINK BUT IT'S GETTING AWFULLY LATE AND I HAVE TO GET UP FOR WORK TOMORROW...

HOW CAN YOU WORK FOR HIM -- THE MAN IS AN OBVIOUS SHAM -- A FRAUD!

HOW DARE YOU, SUH! -- I PAID GOOD MONEY TO BECOME WHAT I AM TODAY

YOU SEE? THERE IS ONLY ONE COURSE OPEN TO US -- YOU AND I -- ONE CHANCE TO SAVE THIS CITY!

WE MUST KILL THIS FOOL -- NOW! THE PEOPLE WILL FOLLOW US -- I KNOW THEY WILL!

NO.

I DON'T SUPPOSE ANYONE WANTS TO HEAR MY OPINION.

BUT WHY? IN THE NAME OF TARIM -- WHY?!!

BECAUSE YOU'RE BOTH IDIOTS! THE ONLY DIFFERENCE IS THAT HE'S FILTHY RICH AND YOU'RE DIRT POOR!

I'M NOT SURE, BUT I THINK I RESENT THAT LAST REMARK!

...OR HE'S REMINDING YOU OF THE IMPORTANCE OF MAKING OUT A WILL.

NGHH NGHH

DON'T MENTION IT.

RGRRNHH! RGGRRNH!

MNRGHH MNRGHH

ATTABOY-- HE MAY BE TALLER AND STRONGER THAN YOU, BUT REMEMBER -- YOU'RE SHORTER AND GRAYER!

ONLY A FEW SECONDS REMAINED BEFORE THE WEIGHT OF THE MAN CARRIED THEM OVER THE EDGE TOWARD CERTAIN DEATH...

FOCUSSING THE REMAINDER OF HIS STRENGTH, CEREBUS PULLS HIS SNOUT IN TIGHT TO HIS FACE...

AND, IN THE NEXT INSTANT, MANAGES TO TWIST INTO THE NECESSARY POSITION!

EARTH-PIG NECK, SHOULDER AND BACK MUSCLES STRAIN AND TENSE BENEATH THE GRAY FUR AND...

DOOMP

UNH?!

PLEASE! ...I...I...

PLEASE!!

I'D ASK YOU TO TEACH THAT TRICK TO THE TROOPS, BUT I DON'T THINK THEY HAVE THE *EQUIPMENT* FOR IT...

WELL, THIS CERTAINLY HAS BEEN QUITE A NIGHT OF ADVENTURE! -- I =SNIFF= I GUESS - =SNIFF?=

IT'S CEREBUS' FUR--THAT ALWAYS HAPPENS WHEN IT GETS WET...

THANK HEAVEN!

I THOUGHT THE ONLIU WERE INVADING!

YOU KNOW -- *CEREBUS* AGREES WITH HIM -- YOU CAN'T KEEP THIS CITY RUNNING IF NO ONE WORKS

WELL -- YOU CAN REST ASSURED THAT I'LL GIVE THE MATTER ALL THE ATTENTION I FEEL IT DESERVES...

THAT'S WHAT CEREBUS WAS AFRAID OF...

CEREBUS IS GOING TO BED...

SO SOON?

YOU CALLED, LORD JULIUS?

CIRCULATE A MEMO...

"ANY MEMBER OF THE HOUSEHOLD STAFF ALLOWING CEREBUS WITHIN TEN FEET OF LORD JULIUS ON A RAINY DAY IS TO BE *EXECUTED!*"

VERY GOOD, SIR!

LORD JULIUS -- FORGIVE THIS *INTRUSION!* SHALL I CALL THE...

LET HIM GO!

I'LL ADMIT IT'S NOT VERY *LIKELY...*

BUT HE MIGHT HAVE SOMETHING INTERESTING TO SAY...

I AM *HERE* LORD JULIUS BECAUSE IT HAS COME TO MY ATTENTION THAT, IN A FORTNIGHT...

...YOU INTEND HAVING *ANOTHER* OF YOUR *DRUNKEN DEBAUCHERIES!*

SORRY -- THE GUEST LIST IS ALREADY SET FOR *THAT* DRUNKEN DEBAUCHERY!

BUT I'LL SPEAK TO MY SOCIAL SECRETARY AND WE'LL TRY TO SQUEEZE YOU IN SOMEWHERE

YOU -- YOU *DARE* TO JEST IN THIS MANNER WITH A PRIEST OF MY *STANDING...?!*

STANDING?

I'M AFRAID THAT'S *IMPOSSIBLE...*

THE ONLY ROOM WE'LL HAVE IS FOR SOMEONE LYING DOWN...

GAH!

WE'LL PENCIL YOU IN FOR *THREE* CUSHIONS BY THE WINE VAT...

AND YOU CAN GIVE US AN ANSWER IN A DAY OR SO...

SEEMED LIKE A DECENT SORT -- WHAT DID YOU THINK?

VERY PRIESTLY. ANY CHANCE HE'LL SHOW UP AT YOUR FESTIVAL?

PROBABLY NOT -- IT'S COUPLES ONLY...

LORD JULIUS...?

SPEAKING.

LORD JULIUS THE MINISTER FOR EXECUTIVE PLANNING REQUESTS AN AUDIENCE...

NOT A CHANCE -- THE LAST TIME I GAVE HIM AN AUDIENCE, HE JUST STOOD THERE AND STUTTERED UNTIL EVERYONE WALKED OUT ON HIM...

NO, NO -- HE WISHES TO *SPEAK* WITH YOU, LORD JULIUS...

WELL, WHY DIDN'T YOU *SAY* SO...?

CANCEL THE AUDIENCE AND SHOW HIM IN...

MINISTER FOR EXECUTIVE PLANNING?

ONE OF MY STENOGRAPHERS... THE CABINET TITLE IS STRICTLY HONORARY...

... IN HONOUR OF WHAT?

IN HONOUR OF HIS PAYING TWO HUNDRED PIECES A MONTH TO USE IT...

I SENT HIM TO THE TORTURE CHAMBER TO RECORD ANY INFORMATION WE CAN SQUEEZE OUT OF THOSE REBELS...

THE MINISTER FOR EXECUTIVE PLANNING, M'LORD!

BASKIN, MY BOY...

COME IN, COME IN'!

READ ME WHAT YOU HAVE SO FAR...

"AAAGH"

"NO, NO, NO"

"AIEEEEE OH-NO, AAG AAAAAH"

"AAAAAAA AAAAGGH!"

"THE PITS"?

...WHAT ARE "THE PITS"?

THE PITS? WHY... THE PITS ARE...

WHEN YOU BOYS ARE THROUGH PLAYING "STUMP THE STENOGRAPHER"...

...LET ME KNOW AND I'LL ORGANIZE SOME NEW GAMES...

ON SECOND THOUGHT, THIS MIGHT BE A GOOD TIME FOR YOU TO TRY OUT YOUR COVER AS KITCHEN STAFF SUPERVISOR...

YOU COULD BASTE THE COOK OR SOMETHING...

I SHOULD HAVE WARNED YOU... LORD JULIUS DOES NOT PERMIT HIS EMPLOYEES TO SPEAK TOGETHER EXCEPT THROUGH HIM...

HE BELIEVES THAT IT CAUSES MUCH DISSATISFACTION IN THE CITY...

HOW DOES ANYTHING GET DONE?

THIS IS A BUREAUCRACY, SIR... NOTHING IS SUPPOSED TO GET DONE!

LORD JULIUS' TANTRUM POSED A PROBLEM FOR CEREBUS! IF HE WAS TO FIND OUT ABOUT "THE PITS" FROM ONE OF THE INNUMERABLE BUREAUCRATS, HE WOULD HAVE TO WAIT 'TIL DUSK WHEN THEY WOULD BE THROUGH PASSING PAPER BACK AND FORTH FOR THE DAY...

"WHERE" MUSED THE EARTH-PIG "CAN I FIND SOMEONE OUTSIDE THE BUREAUCRACY WHO CAN SPARE A FEW MINUTES FOR AN INTERVIEW?"

BLASPHEMERS! YOU ARE ABOMINATIONS IN THE EYES OF THE LIVING TARIM...

REPENT...!

I LOOK ABOUT ME...

AND WHAT IS IT I SEE?

AND WHAT KIND OF EVIL IS IT THAT STILL LIVES AFTER A...?

BLASPHEMY!

UNHOLY!

UNCLEAN!

JEWELRY!

ADORNMENTS!

GRAVEN IMAGES!

OH NO

... CEREBUS THANKS YOU FOR YOUR HELP...

A PRIEST OF TARIM LIVES ONLY TO SERVE.

WASH THAT EVIL PAINT FROM YOUR FACE, UNBELIEVER!!

CAST OFF THESE -- DEMONIC ORNAMENTS!

... AND BEG THE LIVING TARIM FOR FORGIVENESS!

TWAK

BE NOT UNCONSCIOUS BUT OPEN THINE EYES TO THY WICKED WAYS!

TWAK

BE UNCONSCIOUS, THEN, BUT BE NOT DEAD -- OR I SHALL SURELY FACE A MURDER RAP...

CEREBUS MUST SPEAK TO LORD JULIUS ABOUT PRESSING THESE PRIESTS INTO SERVICE AS SHOCK TROOPS...

THE AARDVARK MAKES HIS WAY TO THE ANTE-CHAMBER OF JULIUS' OFFICE, LADEN WITH MAPS, PLANS AND SCROLLS...

EVEN A CURSORY GLANCE THROUGH THE MATERIAL CONFIRMS THE EXISTENCE OF THE PITS! THE PLANS SHOW THE KNOWN PASSAGE-WAYS AND ACCESS ROUTES INTO THEM...

IF CEREBUS' SUSPICIONS PROVED CORRECT, HE KNEW HE WOULD NEED AS COMPLETE A KNOWLEDGE OF THOSE HIDDEN CORRIDORS AS WAS POSSIBLE BEFORE HE EXPLORED THEM...

AH! JUST THE PERSON I WAS LOOKING FOR...

LORD JULIUS -- CEREBUS HAS FOUND SOMETHING ON ALL THESE REVOLUTIONARIES ...

YOU KNOW, THIS ALWAYS HAPPENS WHEN IT'S MY TURN TO STAGE A FESTIVAL...

THE PROBLEM IS, OF COURSE, TO FIND OUT WHERE THEY'RE HIDING...

WHEN YOU'RE SURROUNDED BY BUREAUCRATS, YOU HAVE NO TROUBLE GETTING HALF A TON OF PAPER SHUFFLED FROM ONE END OF THE CITY TO THE OTHER...

TAKING INTO ACCOUNT THEIR MOBILITY, THEIR HIT-AND-RUN TACTICS AND THEIR ORGANISATION ...

BUT ASK THEM TO COME UP WITH AN IDEAL LOCATION FOR *THE FESTIVAL OF PETUNIAS* ...

...AND THESE ARE THE SUGGESTIONS I PAID GOOD MONEY FOR...

THERE'S ONLY ONE PLACE IN THE CITY THAT COULD CONCEAL THAT MANY PEOPLE...

"THE BALLROOM... THE BALLROOM ...THE CENTRAL PLAZA... THE BALLROOM...,THE BALLROOM..."

THROWING CAUTION TO THE WIND I THOUGHT MAYBE *YOU* MIGHT HAVE AN IDEA...

...THE PITS!

OF COURSE! *THE PITS!*

OH, MOTHER! WHAT AN IDEA! OLD LEOPOLD THOUGHT NO ONE WOULD EVER TOP HIS FESTIVAL OF GROUNDHOGS IN A LIVE VOLCANO!

WHAT A PARTY THIS WILL BE!

PARTY?

LORD JULIUS -- CEREBUS WAS TALKING ABOUT...

"THE PETUNIAS IN THE PITS!"

I WONDER IF IT'S TOO LATE TO WALLPAPER!

WELL, NO TIME LIKE THE PRESENT TO CHECK OUT WHAT WE HAVE TO WORK WITH...

OH, BASKIN!

M'LORD?

SAY-- WHAT ARE YOU DOING BACK THERE?

YOU FORGOT TO DISMISS ME THIS AFTERNOON AFTER I READ MY NOTES, M'LORD...

THAT EXPLAINS WHY THE MATTRESS WAS LUMPY WHEN I TOOK MY NAP...

WELL, NEVER MIND THAT! I'LL NEED YOU TO TAKE DICTATION WHEN I CHECK OUT THE PITS...

YOU BOYS WAIT HERE WHILE I SLIP INTO SOME LESS-EXPENSIVE SHOES...

VERY GOOD, M'LORD!

CEREBUS DOESN'T THINK YOU LOOK VERY WELL...

FRIGHTENED OF THE PITS? WHY THE VERY IDEA! DO YOU TAKE ME FOR A CHILD--? PTOO! I SPIT ON THE SHADOW-CRAWLER-THOSE ARE JUST STORIES TO FRIGHTEN CHILDREN! DEVOURING MEN IN ONE BITE! WHO COULD PICTURE SUCH A THING?

LORD JULIUS-- CEREBUS WILL BE NEEDING A SWORD...

I MEAN THE WHOLE IDEA IS SILLY ISN'T IT? HAHAHAA? ISN'T IT? HUH ...WELL?

YOU CAN USE MINE ....

GUARD IT WITH YOUR LIFE--THERE'S THE JUICE OF A THOUSAND GRAPEFRUIT ON THAT BLADE...

JUICE...YES!

GRAPEFRUIT!

HAHAHA!

FIND OUT WHAT HE'S BEEN SMOKING...

AND HAVE A FEW OUNCES SENT TO MY CHAMBER...

HE WAS JUST TELLING CEREBUS SOME FOLK TALES ABOUT *THE PITS* HE REMEMBERED FROM HIS CHILDHOOD...

SILLY--YES! SILLY--SILLY FOLK TALES.

ABOUT-THE-PITS...

MOMENTS LATER, THE TRIO DESCENDS INTO A DARKNESS AS SUFFOCATING AS IT IS SILENT...

FIRST OF ALL, WE'RE GOING TO NEED A WORK-CREW TO SCRAPE THIS GRAY SLIME OFF THE WALLS...

WASN'T IT PARMOC THAT SENT US THE MESSAGE OF A POSSIBLE FOOD SHORTAGE THIS WINTER?

YES M'LORD

HAVE THE SLIME GARNISHED WITH FRUIT SLICES AND DELIVERED BY CARAVAN WITH MY COMPLIMENTS...

SOMETHING IS AMISS!

NO--I'M PRETTY SURE...

FRUIT SLICES WITH GRAY SLIME... NO DOUBT ABOUT IT...!

THAT DOOR... ON THE PLANS IT WAS MARKED AS BEING BLOCKED BY TEN FEET OF RUBBLE ....

THIS IS AN *OUTRAGE!* YOU MEAN, SOMEONE HAS STOLEN TEN FEET OF *MY* RUBBLE?

...OR...

...EATEN IT.

DON'T BE *ABSURD!* THE PEASANTS ARE HUNGRY...

...BUT THEY'RE NOT *THAT* HUNGRY...

COME ALONG, BASKIN! IF THAT RUBBLE THIEF IS STILL AROUND, HE'S GOING TO RUE THE DAY HE TANGLED WITH US!

STAY CLOSE TOGETHER-- THIS MAY BE A TRAP...

M-MAYHAP WE SHOULD TURN BACK

I DON'T LIKE TO DISILLUSION YOU BOYS, BUT ANYONE STUPID ENOUGH TO STEAL RUBBLE COULDN'T BE SMART ENOUGH TO CONSTRUCT A REALLY SOPHISTICATED...

CLANG

CLANG

HELP.

GREETINGS...

...AS THE LEADER OF THE "EYE OF THE PYRAMID" I BID WELCOME TO THE SOON-TO-BE-DEPARTED LORD JULIUS OF PALNU AND HIS...

...COMPANIONS.

MAYHAP YOU HAVEN'T NOTICED....

BUT ONE OF YOUR RABBITS ISN'T IN HIS HUTCH...

INTENTIONAL, I ASSURE YOU ...WHEN I SAW YOU CARRYING A SWORD, I ASSUMED YOU WERE LORD JULIUS'...

...CHAMPION?

LORD JULIUS' EMPLOYEE...

...IF YOU COME DOWN HERE IT WILL SAVE CEREBUS THE TROUBLE OF DISMANTLING THAT WALL...

FOR A THOUSAND YEARS HAS THE PYRAMID SURVIVED...

AND, FOR A THOUSAND YEARS...

THERE HAS BEEN BUT ONE FATE FOR THE UNBELIEVER...

THE SHADOW-CRAWLER'S HIDE SEEMED VULNERABLE ENOUGH-- LIKE A SYNTHESIS OF LEATHER AND SNAKE SKIN. EVEN AS THE CREATURE LUNGES, CEREBUS CROUCHES LOW...

...AND DIVES UNDER THE ATTACK...

USING HIS FORWARD MOMENTUM, THE EARTH-PIG FLIPS ONCE...

...AND LANDS ON HIS FEET! ARMS RIGID, AND GRIPPING THE SWORD WITH BOTH HANDS, HE DELIVERS A TREMENDOUS BLOW TO THE CREATURE'S EXPOSED FLANK...

THE NET RESULT OF WHICH IS A SHOOTING PAIN IN THE AARDVARK'S RIGHT WRIST AND A SOMEWHAT ANGRIER SHADOW-CRAWLER...

HIS SWORD AT THE READY, CEREBUS PREPARES TO STRIKE AGAIN...

THIS TIME AT THE UNBLINKING RIGHT EYE...

WHICH, IF ANYTHING, PROVES TO BE TOUGHER THAN THE HIDE...

THE EARTH-PIG'S REFLEXES BUY HIM ANOTHER SECOND OF LIFE

...AND HIS MIND RACES...

... THE CREATURE IS SORCEROUS...

...ITS HIDE IS IMPENETRABLE...

...IT HAS NO WEAKNESS...

THE TORCHES FORM TWO LINES ON THE TUNNEL WALLS...

AND IT IS THIS LAST THOUGHT WHICH GIVES CEREBUS THE KEY TO THEIR ESCAPE...

HIS SWORD WAS OF NO USE...

...FOR GOOD OR ILL...

...THREE LIVES NOW HINGED...

...ON TWO SLIM TORCHES!

FOR CENTURIES, THE CRAWLER HAD PERCEIVED LITTLE IN HIS ENVIRONMENT, SAVE THE DOUBLE ROW OF TORCHES WHICH INVARIABLY LED HIM TO FOOD...

...THIS TIME AS HE LUNGES...

...ONE OF THE TORCHES **MOVES!**

AT THE LAST INSTANT, WITHIN INCHES OF THE FLAME, THE CREATURE VEERS AWAY...

IN THAT INSTANT, CEREBUS IS ON THE CREATURE'S BACK... NOW **TWO** TORCHES BEGIN TO MOVE...

FOR A MOMENT, THE SHADOW-CRAWLER IS CONFUSED-- UNTIL CEREBUS MOVES THE FLAMES INTO POSITION ...

...ON EITHER SIDE OF THE MASSIVE HEAD...INSTINCTS TAKE OVER AND THE CRAWLER ABRUPTLY ACCELERATES...

...TOWARDS ITS PREY!

AND CEREBUS HOPES, AS THE WALL LEAPS FORWARD...

NO!

...THAT THE IMPACT WILL BE SUFFICIENT...

NO!

...TO KNOCK THE BEAST SENSELESS!

NOO!

AAAAH!

BAM

TOO BAD THE BARS DIDN'T GO BACK WHERE THEY CAME FROM UNTIL YOU HIT THE WALL...

OTHERWISE I COULD HAVE HELPED YOU WITH THAT OVERSIZED PORTION OF FISH-BAIT!

THAT RUMBLING!

SPEAKING OF FISH--IT LOOKS LIKE EVERYONE'S FAVOURITE REVOLUTIONARY AND SNAKE FETISHIST IS DEPARTING THE PREMISES...

WE'LL HAVE TO WORRY ABOUT HIM LATER, LORD JULIUS...

CEREBUS SEEMS TO HAVE LOOSENED A PIVOTAL PIECE OF ARCHITECTURE...

THE SHORT EXPANSE OF FLOOR STRETCHES BEFORE THEM AS STONE CONTINUES TO DROP IN EVER-LARGER PIECES...

AND JUST AS THE CEILING SHRUGS AND GIVES UP IN ITS CENTURIES-OLD COMPETITION WITH GRAVITY...

...THEY ARE OUTSIDE OF THE TUNNEL...

...EACH, MORE OR LESS, ALIVE...

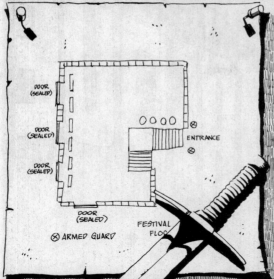

synopsis:

THE ATTACKS ON THE BUREAUCRACY BY THE REVOLUTIONARIES KNOWN ONLY AS THE EYE OF THE PYRAMID HAVE BECOME EVEN MORE FREQUENT! AS THE FESTIVAL OF PETUNIAS NEARS, CEREBUS IS FACED WITH MAKING THE PITS INTO A SAFE LOCATION FOR THE FESTIVITIES! HE INSISTS, OVER LORD JULIUS' GRUMBLING THAT THE GUEST LIST AND FESTIVAL AREA BE CUT IN HALF AND ONLY ONE ENTRANCE BE LEFT UNSEALED! EVEN WITH THESE PRECAUTIONS, THERE IS NO GUARANTEE OF SAFETY! IF A POTENTIAL ASSASSIN WAS **ON** THE GUEST LIST, HE COULD EASILY STRIKE DOWN THE GRANDLORD OF PALNU AND ESCAPE IN THE CONFUSION! IT IS THE EARTH-PIG'S HOPE THAT JULIUS HAS HEEDED HIS WARNINGS AND WILL KEEP HIMSELF AT A REASONABLE DISTANCE FROM THE CROWD OF PARTY-GOERS...

WHAT ARE YOU SUPPOSED TO *BE* ANYWAY...?

AN AARDVARK WEARING A FURRY BLACK SHIRT...

WELL, YOU'VE GOT MY VOTE FOR "MOST AUTHENTIC COSTUME"...

CEREBUS KNEW THAT, BARELY A HUNDRED YARDS AWAY, MEN WERE STILL SEARCHING THE RUBBLE FOR THE REBEL LEADER'S CORPSE. THE EARTH-PIG WAS CERTAIN THEY WOULDN'T FIND IT...

AH! LORD AND LADY WYNDMEL-SMITH...

...YOU'VE MET *CEREBUS*, MY KITCHEN STAFF SUPERVISOR...?

WHY... NO!

...WE HAVEN'T HAD THE PLEASURE ...HOW DO YOU DO?

CEREBUS HAS NO TIME FOR FAT LADIES...

THERE MAY BE REBELS ABOUT...

I'VE BEEN THINKING THAT HE MIGHT BE A CANDIDATE FOR THAT DIPLOMATIC LIASON POST IN PANROVY...

YOU DON'T SAY...

I...I...uh...I

IF YOU'LL EXCUSE ME, I'M GOING TO TRY TO CATCH UP TO HIM BEFORE HE GETS ME INTO A WAR...

BY ALL MEANS... AND I'LL SEE IF I CAN FIND SOMEONE TO GET ARISTONNIA'S HEART STARTED AGAIN...

THERE YOU ARE!

YOU HAVEN'T TALKED TO ANYONE, HAVE YOU?

JUST SOME WOODEN-HEADED BUREAUCRAT WITH A LISP...

uh -- WAS HE WEARING A FALCON'S HEAD?.

AYE! CEREBUS TOLD HIM WHAT TO DO WITH HIS BEAK...

WELL, ESHNOSOPUR NEVER WAS THAT GOOD AN ALLY...

LORD JULIUS...

...THERE IS MENACE IN THE AIR HERE...

THAT'S JUST THE HERRING-AND-ONION DIP... TRY FACING AWAY FROM THE AIR DUCTS...

"CEREBUS KNOWS THIS AREA IS SECURE, LORD JULIUS..."

"THOSE GUARDS WON'T LET ANYONE IN WITHOUT AN INVITATION"

"BUT CEREBUS CAN'T HELP FEELING..."

"... WE'VE OVERLOOKED SOMETHING!"

E'LASS! IT'S HIM! IT'S THE-KILLER-WHO-LOOKS-LIKE-A-BUNNY!

SH! THESE TWO INVITATIONS TOOK THE LAST OF OUR MONEY!

IF YOU GET US THROWN OUT, WE LOSE OUR CHANCE AT THE WYNDMEL DIAMOND

AND WITHOUT THAT DIAMOND WE DON'T HAVE ANY MONEY FOR FOOD...

BUT E'LASS -- WHAT IF HE RECOGNIZES ME? HE DOESN'T LIKE ME -- I CAN TELL BY THE WAY HE PUNCHES ME WHENEVER I GET NEAR HIM...*

* CEREBUS #6

JUST KEEP THAT MASK ON, DON'T TALK...

...AND TRY NOT TO MOVE AROUND...

WITH ANY LUCK HE'LL FIGURE YOU'RE A BABY ELM THAT SOMEONE DRESSED UP AS A JOKE...

WHY, LORD JULIUS -- WHAT AN ADORABLE COSTUME...

THIS OLD THING? I HAD IT PATTERNED ON THE BURIAL COSTUME OF DESERAN THE GAUCHE...

TEE-HEE! YOU SAY THE CUTEST THINGS...

IT'S HIM!

HE'S EVEN WEARING THE SAME ROBES!

THEY SAY HALF OF THE FUNERAL PARTY WAS NAUSEOUS FOR A WEEK...

DON'T I THOUGH?

UNH?

THE SITUATION WAS HOPELESS THE EARTH-PIG HAD DECIDED...

...EVEN IF THE LEADER OF THE REVOLUTION WAS HERE, HE COULD BE WEARING...

CEREBUS PAUSED.

PERHAPS IT WAS A TRICK...

...A DECOY IN BLACK ROBES TO DRAW HIM AWAY FROM LORD JULIUS...

THE EARTH-PIG SUDDENLY FELT *VULNERABLE* ...THEY WERE IN THE MIDST OF THE CROWD, FAR FROM THE STONE WALLS AND STAIRWAY...

TACTICALLY, THEIR POSITION WAS A *DISASTER*...

A MOTION TO THE RIGHT CATCHES CEREBUS' ATTENTION...

GRADUALLY HE BECOMES AWARE THAT THERE ARE ABOUT A DOZEN AMONG THE GUESTS WATCHING HIM INTENTLY...

EACH IS CARRYING A SWORD, AND, STEP-BY-CAUTIOUS-STEP, ...

...EACH IS GETTING CLOSER AND CLOSER TO HIM...

HE OPENS HIS MOUTH TO CALL THE GUARDS FROM THEIR POST AT THE ENTRANCE...

UNTIL HE SEES THEM IN THE CROWD, SIDE-BY-SIDE WITH THE REBELS, THEIR SWORDS DRAWN AND SMILES OF BARELY CONCEALED AMUSEMENT ON THEIR FACES

I DON'T WISH TO INTERRUPT LORD JULIUS BUT ARMED REBELS ARE ADVANCING ON US...

WELL, DON'T JUST *STAND* THERE -- *DO* SOMETHING...

CEREBUS IS OPEN TO SUGGESTIONS

HIS SWORD WOULD BE USELESS AGAINST A DOZEN OPPONENTS! HIS ONLY CHANCE WOULD BE TO GET THE FESTIVAL GUESTS TO TURN ON THE ARMED REVOLUTIONARIES SOMEHOW...

BUT CEREBUS HAD SEEN ENOUGH OF RICH CITY-DWELLERS TO KNOW THAT THEIR INSTINCTIVE REACTION TO ANY WARNING OF DANGER WOULD BE A MINDLESS, FULL-SCALE PANIC...

AND, OUT IN THE OPEN LIKE THIS, A MASS EXODUS TO THE STAIRWAY WOULD FINISH THEM AS SURELY AS THE REBELS' SWORDS...

EVEN IF HE *COULD* ROUSE A FEW OF THE JADED MERCHANTS TO AID HIM, THE MATERIAL IMMEDIATELY AVAILABLE WAS NOT EXACTLY INSPIRING...

HEMMED IN NEXT TO THE REFRESHMENT TABLES, CEREBUS BEGINS TO THINK THAT THE LAST SOUND HE WOULD EVER HEAR WOULD BE THE GRINDING OF MOLARS...

TARIM! IT WOULD TAKE A CROWBAR TO PRY THEIR FEEBLE MINDS AWAY FROM THAT FOUL-SMELLING...

PERHAPS I COULD GET YOU SOME OF THAT DIP WE HAD EARLIER...?

LUCIUS! THE DIP! NOW I KNOW WHAT THE WRETCHED CREATURE HAS PLANNED—HE'S GOING TO POISON US ALL!

HE PROBABLY STIRRED IT WITH THOSE LICE-INFESTED HANDS OF HIS,...AND ...I ...I...... ...ATE...

OOOOOOOOOOH

PERHAPS JUST THE BRANDY, THEN...

DON'T GO AWAY, MY DEAR...

ELASS CHEWED HIS LIP NERVOUSLY BENEATH HIS MASK... HE TRIED TO PUSH ALL THOUGHTS OF LORD JULIUS' BOARD OF JUSTICE FROM HIS MIND ...

THE INFREQUENT INCIDENTS OF CRIME IN PALNU WAS DUE IN LARGE PART TO THIS AUGUST BODY RENOWNED FOR THEIR WISDOM, EXPERIENCE...

..AND UNBLEMISHED RECORD OF THREE THOUSAND TWO HUNDRED AND EIGHTY-ONE CONVICTIONS IN THREE THOUSAND TWO HUNDRED AND EIGHTY-ONE TRIALS...

GINGERLY LIFTING THE DIAMOND WITH ONE HAND, HIS RESOLVE CRUMBLES! WHAT IF SOMEONE WAS WATCHING HIM? HE HADN'T PLANNED THOROUGHLY ENOUGH--BETTER TO GET OUT NOW! IF THEY NEEDED MONEY, TURG WOULD JUST HAVE TO GET A ...

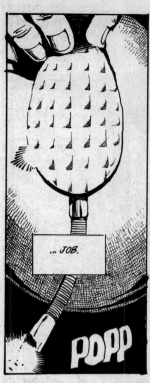

... JOB.

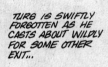

POPP

THE BUTTERFLIES IN HIS STOMACH BECAME FANGED LIZARDS... HE HAD SEEN LORD JULIUS' GUARDS AT THE ENTRANCE...

LORD WYNDMEL MIGHT RETURN AT ANY MOMENT

THERE WAS SIMPLY NO TIME TO REATTACH THE GEM...

HE BECAME EVEN MORE CONVINCED SOMEONE WAS WATCHING HIM! "THAT'S RIGHT, HE TOOK IT RIGHT OFF HER WRIST!" "HE'S NOTHING BUT A LITTLE THIEF! OFF WITH HIS HEAD!"

TURG IS SWIFTLY FORGOTTEN AS HE CASTS ABOUT WILDLY FOR SOME OTHER EXIT...

IT WAS SAID THAT LORD JULIUS' GUARDS WERE TRAINED TO RECOGNISE THE SCENT OF GUILT SEVERAL FEET AWAY...

CEREBUS SCANNED THE CROWD THROUGH A HERRING AND ONION BLUR... WITH THE FAILURE OF HIS ASSASSINS, THE REBEL LEADER WAS DOUBTLESS EVEN NOW CRAWLING BACK UNDER SOME CONVENIENT ROCK...

LORD JULIUS! OVER THERE!

EH? OVER...

OHO!

A FEELING BEGINS TO GNAW AT E'LASS' NERVES THAT THERE **WAS** ONLY ONE EXIT...

LADY WYNDMEL WAS ALREADY STIRRING ON HER COUCH! E'LASS WHIMPERED...THERE JUST **HAD** TO BE...

...A WAY OUT...

I GUESS IT'S **TRUE**

TARIM **DOES** HELP THE PURE OF HEART...

LOCKED IN CONVERSATION, CEREBUS AND LORD JULIUS FAIL TO SEE THE SECOND FIGURE SLIP QUIETLY AWAY FROM THE FESTIVITIES...

WELL?

AREN'T YOU GOING **AFTER** HIM?

CEREBUS THINKS YOU BETTER COME ALONG, TOO

ME? WHY?

BECAUSE THOSE ASSASSINS ARE GOING TO BE A TRIFLE PEEVISH WHEN THE CROWD RUNS OUT OF DIP...

AND THEY'VE **ALREADY** BEEN ORDERED TO KILL YOU...

SAY-- DO YOU MIND IF I COME ALONG?

CEREBUS WOULD BE MOST PLEASED ...

USING HIS COSTUME TO CONCEAL HIS SWORD FROM THE CROWD, CEREBUS LEADS LORD JULIUS TO THE SLIDING STONE PANEL...

E'LASS CONFRONTS THE STONE CORRIDOR BEFORE HIM WITH APPREHENSION... BARELY A DOZEN FEET AWAY IS INKY BLACKNESS

HIS MIND MULLS OVER THE POSSIBILITY OF RETURNING TO THE FESTIVAL AND DROPPING THE DIAMOND ON THE FLOOR --THEN PRAYING NO ONE SEES HIM DO IT...

...BUT IN THE FEW SECONDS IT TAKES TO WEIGH HIS OPTIONS...

THROUGH HERE-- HE'S ONLY HAD A FEW SECONDS HEAD START...

THE DECISION IS MADE FOR HIM...

WHY NOT JUST LET HIM GO? WE CAN BRING A DOZEN MEN IN HERE TOMORROW TO DESTROY ANYTHING THAT MOVES...

HE'S MADE A FOOL OF CEREBUS FOR THE LAST TIME... CEREBUS IS GOING TO FOLLOW HIM...

...AND ONE OF ISN'T COMING OUT OF HERE ALIVE...

OH, MIGHTY TARIM -- YOUR HUMBLE SERVANT BESEECHES YOU TO BE MERCIFUL AND STRIKE DOWN HIS ENEMIES WITH MASSIVE CORONARIES ...

SO TURG HAD BEEN RIGHT... IT HAD TAKEN MORE THAN A YEAR, BUT IT SEEMED CEREBUS WAS JUST AS ANGRY AS HE...

E'LASS COULD BARELY CONTAIN HIS AMAZEMENT! THEY HAD GONE RIGHT PAST HIM, AS IF IT HAD NEVER OCCURRED TO THEM THAT HE MIGHT BE HIDING...

E'LASS FELT HIS HEART SWELL WITH PURITY.... IN A FEW SECONDS, THEY WOULD BE GONE...LOOKING FOR HIM!

WITH HIS NEWLY-DEVELOPED BOND WITH TARIM, E'LASS WAS CONVINCED HE COULD WALK PAST JULIUS' GUARDS WITHOUT A...

THOOM

TARIM! WHAT WAS THAT?

THE SLIDING PANEL...

AYE!

CLOSED TIGHT...

UNDOUBTEDLY, A SIGN THAT OUR QUARRY SEEKS A CONFRONTATION AS MUCH AS CEREBUS DOES...

NO! NO! I DON'T! REALLY -- WE COULD BE FRIENDS! I'LL EVEN GIVE BACK THE DIAMOND...

As the sound of footsteps fades to a distant echo, E'lass steals once more from his hiding place...

PLEASE, TARIM!

YOU DID IT ONCE--JUST OPEN THE PANEL...

I'LL USE THE DIAMOND TO BUILD CHURCHES --MONASTERIES

PLEASE OPEN IT.... PLEEEASE!

He had come this far... he refused to give up! He forced his mind to slow down and THINK...!

Somewhere up ahead there HAD to be a doorway or tunnel that would lead him to the surface...

Clenching his teeth he resolves to find it...

And when he found it -- with or WITHOUT Tarim's help...

He would be a very wealthy man...

YOU REALLY THINK HE KNOWS WE'RE CHASING HIM?

WE'RE NO LONGER CHASING HIM, LORD JULIUS ...

WE'RE BEING LED!

LED? BUT HOW COULD HE...?

FROM THE TIME WE CAME THROUGH THAT *PANEL*, WE HAVEN'T ONCE BEEN FACED WITH A CHOICE OF PATHS TO FOLLOW...

THERE HAVE BEEN NO SIDE-TUNNELS, NO DOORWAYS, NO BRIDGES...

IT IS VERY MUCH UNLIKE THE PREY TO LEAD YOU TO HIS HIDING SPOT

BUT IT IS *NOT* SO UNLIKE THE PREDATOR...

HE IS UP AHEAD-- SOMEWHERE-- WAITING FOR US!

THERE WEREN'T ANY SIDE TUNNELS! HE HAD WALKED FOR THE EQUIVALENT OF FIVE CITY BLOCKS! WHAT IF THE TUNNEL ENDED UP AHEAD? THEY MIGHT ALREADY HAVE TURNED BACK! IF SO, HE WAS *TRAPPED*!

I'D PROBABLY BE ABLE TO HANDLE THIS BETTER IF MY STOMACH DIDN'T HURT SO MUCH...

GREETINGS, GENTLE-MEN -- I'VE REALIZED THAT THE SHADOW-CRAWLER WAS A --uh-- MISTAKE...

LARGE, POWERFUL, BUT IN *ESSENCE* LITTLE MORE THAN A TRIBAL MASCOT THAT PROVED UNSUITED TO ITS TASK... *

* CEREBUS #15

NO -- THERE IS ONLY ONE WAY TO SETTLE THIS SITUATION! UNTIL YOU ARE DEAD LORD JULIUS, MY FORCES WILL BE LITTLE MORE THAN THE DREGS OF YOUR OWN SOCIETY -- THE MALCONTENTS!

... WITH YOU DEAD, PALNU WILL NEED A NEW LEADER ... THOSE WHO NOW FEAR YOUR POWER AND INFLUENCE ...

WILL FEAR NO LONGER! I WILL TRAMPLE YOUR DAMN BUREAUCRACY INTO DUST!

IN A FEW WEEKS LORD JULIUS' REIGN WILL BE LITTLE MORE THAN A BAD DREAM ...

IN THE MINDS OF THE PEOPLE OF PALNU ...

... MY PEOPLE.

YOU ARE ALL THAT STANDS IN MY WAY, CEREBUS! STEP FORWARD AND FIGHT FOR WHAT LITTLE HONOUR YOUR MASTER STILL RETAINS ...

WHAT ARE YOU WAITING FOR ...?

DON'T YOU KNOW IT'S IMPOLITE TO KEEP A PSYCHOTIC WAITING?

CEREBUS IS TIRED OF CITIES ... PALNU, BEDUIN THEY ARE ALL THE SAME!

CEREBUS NEEDS MORE THAN MODIFIED ANT-HILLS CAN OFFER ...

THIS IS A HELL OF A TIME TO DECIDE TO ASK FOR A RAISE!

CEREBUS WILL FIGHT YOUR BATTLE, BUT CEREBUS WANTS EIGHT BAGS OF GOLD AND A HORSE SO HE CAN GET OUT OF THIS ...

DO YOU HAVE ANY IDEA OF THE DENT THAT WOULD PUT IN MY PETTY CASH VAULT? I REFUSE!

THE PSYCHOTIC'S QUARREL IS WITH YOU! IF YOU PREFER, CEREBUS WILL GO NOW, EMPTY-HANDED ...

... AND LEAVE YOU TWO TO SETTLE YOUR DIFFERENCES ...

LORD JULIUS WATCHES THE HORSE AND RIDER PASS FROM SIGHT... "WHERE DO YOU THINK YOU'LL GO?" "NORTH--SOUTH... IT MATTERS LITTLE WHEN YOU'RE RICH" AND THAT WAS IT, TOO BAD, REALLY... WHO KNOWS WHAT HE MIGHT HAVE BEEN ABLE TO DO FOR PALNU...? AS A GENERAL, HE COULD POSSIBLY HAVE...

MESSAGE FOR YOU, LORD JULIUS...

HAVE YOU GOT CHANGE FOR A GOLD PIECE?

OH, YES, SIR!

GOOD, THEN YOU WON'T NEED THIS COPPER BIT I WAS GOING TO GIVE YOU

happy to he is well...

kitchen sta sounds very a friend I year ago Cerebus...

I will be ar a few days I look forw eeing him a

niece, Jaka

DEAR UNCLE JULIUS:

I am sorry I w unable to attend your festival... I that it was a suc and that you wi in your heart to me for missing an event

As for your re tter. I was ve

Take care

HEY!

OH, WELL...

IT PROBABLY WASN'T IMPORTANT....